REDUCING LOSSES IN

HIGH RISK FLOOD HAZARD AREAS:

A GUIDEBOOK FOR LOCAL OFFICIALS

D1369294

Prepared by

The Association of State Floodplain Managers

for

The Federal Emergency Management Agency

1985

The opinions expressed are those of the authors and not necessarily those of the Federal Emergency Management Agency or the Association of State Floodplain Managers.

PREFACE

As indicated by its title, this publication is intended to provide guidance to local officials in their efforts to reduce flood losses in high risk flood areas.

Since some of these high risk flood areas have not been specifically identified by the Federal Insurance Administration, the implementation of appropriate floodplain management criteria for those areas is not required for participation in the National Flood Insurance Program. However, for those communities which have experienced losses to life and property in those high risk flood areas and which have an interest in addressing those hazards, the community options and management strategies which follow are available for their consideration and, where appropriate, their use. The community options, with accompanying examples of adopted local/state measures, or suggested model ordinance language, should provide useful guidance to the local decision maker.

The Federal Insurance Administration believes that reducing flood damages in high risk flood hazard areas can and should be addressed at the local or state level. Therefore, while not a condition of participation in the National Flood Insurance Program, the use of these community options and management strategies is encouraged. This guidebook should greatly facilitate that effort.

HOW TO USE THIS GUIDEBOOK

This guidebook has been prepared to help local governments improve the effectiveness of their floodplain management programs for high risk flood hazard areas. It is designed to:

1. Identify general areas where special risks are posed to life and property due to the depth, velocity and duration of flooding, debris in the water or other factors.

2. Describe a process for amending existing regulations or adopting new regulations for high risk areas.

3. Provide examples of innovative community programs and approaches for high risk areas.

4. Direct guidebook users to sources of more detailed information on high risk areas.

Chapter 1 of this guidebook gives an overview of nine types of high risk areas. Chapter 2 explains the importance of managing high risk areas and describes generic options and steps for improving their management. Chapters 3 through 11 provide descriptions and guidance for managing development in high risk areas. All chapters follow a common framework, where each of these items is included if appropriate:

> The Hazard
>
> Existing Mitigation Efforts
>
> Options for Action
>
> > Policy and Program Elements
> >
> > Mapping
> >
> > Regulatory Action
> >
> > Nonregulatory Action
>
> Selected References
>
> Appendices

Appendices contain examples of ordinances, regulations, guidelines and descriptions of community programs.

TABLE OF CONTENTS

CHAPTER 1: THE HIGH RISK AREAS

Anytown, USA -- The sun sinks behind the hills, giving way to a sky full of stars. As the lights of town darken, so does the sky. Thunder rumbles faintly in the nearby mountains. The rumble becomes a roar. Blinding rain pelts the landscape for an hour; then a second hour. Dry land becomes a rushing river, carrying trees, boulders and mud. The next morning's sunrise reveals that homes several blocks from the river are undercut by deep gullies. Countless basements and first floors are filled with mud and debris. Not a store window remains intact on Main Street.

We all know that flooding can have dramatically different impacts in different areas. Our example illustrates some of the characteristics of high risk flooding. There are four in all:

High velocity

Debris in the flood water

Suddenness

Long duration

Under one or a combination of these conditions, buildings seldom just get wet. They are severely damaged or destroyed. Reuse of the flooded land may be difficult.

All fifty states have high risk flood hazard areas. Preliminary estimates show that 20 to 25 percent of the nations's floodplains are high risk areas. Much of the current floodplain development is concentrated in these areas. The total flood risk in the U.S. is increasing as more people build on and live in these areas. Development also increases the level of risk on adjacent lands by altering natural hydrologic conditions (e.g., restricting stream channels, increasing runoff or changing slopes and stream gradients).

In this guidebook, we explain the risks - and suggest possible risk reduction techniques - for nine types of high risk flood hazard areas not presently addressed in most state and local programs. Floodways and coastal velocity zones are not considered in this guidebook because they are already regulated by many states and local governments.

ALLUVIAL FANS

An estimated 20 to 30 percent of the land in the Southwest consists of deposits of soil washed down from mountain slopes in fan-like deposits. These include many urban areas such as Los Angeles County and Clark County (Las Vegas). Often the entire fan is at high risk because of the high velocity of the water, erosion and drainage channels meandering across the surface of the fan.

AREAS BEHIND UNSAFE OR INADEQUATE LEVEES

Twenty-five thousand miles of levees line streams and rivers throughout the United States. Breaching or overtopping of levees causes unexpected floods that are deep and have high velocity. When levees are overtopped, floodwaters are held back from returning to the river and inundation is prolonged .

AREAS BELOW UNSAFE OR INADEQUATE DAMS

More than 2000 communities are at risk from dams that have been identified as unsafe. Even dams classified as safe may be overtopped or breached by extraordinary floods, earthquakes, or improper maintenance. Flooding from breaching or overtopping is often deep, of high velocity and likely to occur with little or no warning.

COASTAL FLOODING AND EROSION AREAS

Erosion and flooding combine to increase flood damage along thousands of miles of coastline. The most serious problems are on barrier islands, along the Great Lakes shoreline and along the Gulf coast. Erosion removes natural protective barriers - beaches, dunes and bluffs - causing direct damage as well as exposing buildings to larger waves and storm surges.

FLASH FLOOD AREAS

Although they may occur in all fifty states, flash floods are most common in the arid and semi-arid west where there is steep topography, little vegetation and intense but short-duration rainfall. They rank first as a cause of flood-related deaths in the United States. Heavy rains, sometimes in combination with spring snowmelt, often lead to rapidly rising, fast moving water which can cause severe erosion as well as flood damage. Flash floods occur in both urban and rural settings, principally along smaller rivers and drainageways.

FLOODING DUE TO GROUND FAILURE: SUBSIDENCE AND LIQUEFACTION

Subsidence occurs in parts of all fifty states. The problem is particularly serious in southern California, the Houston-Galveston area and southern Louisiana. Lowering of the land surface - caused by extraction of subsurface fluids and other materials, soil compaction or other processes - can increase flood depths and duration.

Liquefaction occurs when unconsolidated sands and silts temporarily flow like thick fluids, usually triggered by earthquakes. Liquefaction can be a major cause of flooding if dams or levees are damaged or if structures on filled wetlands sink below water level.

FLUCTUATING LAKE LEVELS

Thousands of inland lakes, including the Great Lakes and the Great Salt Lake, are subject to long-term fluctuations in water levels. Recent fluctuations of the Great Salt Lake have caused over one hundred million dollars in losses in a single year. Lake levels can rise and remain high for years, with damage compounded by ice and shore erosion and detrimental impacts on water quality.

ICE JAMS

Thirty-five northern and midwestern states suffer high risk flooding due to ice jams. Dams of ice increase flood levels upstream, then unleash ice floes and deep, high velocity floodwaters downstream. The combination of ice, debris and water can cause tremendous physical damage to structures.

MUDSLIDES

Heavy rains can trigger mudfloods or mudflows in areas of steep slope, limited vegetation and unconsolidated soils. Flows can be sudden and deep, but the greatest damage is often done by the debris. Mudflows and mudfloods are a particular problem in Southern California, the San Francisco Bay area and the communities surrounding the Great Salt Lake.

WHY UPGRADE EXISTING PLANS AND REGULATIONS?

Existing community maps and regulations for flood hazard areas often provide inadequate protection for high risk areas. Most local regulations, adopted to implement state and federal floodplain management guidelines, are designed to address normal flood hazards. Here the depth of inundation is the primary factor causing damage and waters are relatively free of sediment and debris. Flooding is temporary and the configuration of the flood channel is relatively stable. Areas subject to normal flood hazards include low velocity flow areas along major rivers and streams and relatively flat coastal areas inundated by the storm surge where waves and erosion are not major factors.

State and national criteria based upon such a concept of the "norm" have proven satisfactory for 70 to 80 percent of the country. However, the failure to consider other flood damage factors has resulted in serious deficiencies in management approaches for the high risk areas, including the following:

Maps usually understate hazards in areas with velocity, debris or other high risk problems. For example, flood maps for alluvial fan areas designating them as shallow flooding areas incorrectly imply low risk. Usually the risks there are quite serious due to high velocities, debris and erosion.

Regulatory criteria designed for the "norm" also underestimate the hazard from high velocity flow, erosion, debris loading and duration of inundation. This can result in damage or destruction of structures built in compliance with regulatory criteria.

THE HIGH RISK FACTORS

Depth of inundation is the basic cause of damage in most floods and is also an important factor in high risk areas. Factors that cause additional damages in high risk areas include:

High velocity. The damage potential of flood waters increases dramatically, sometimes exponentially, with velocity. Velocity is determined by slope, waves and several other factors. Unless the potential for high velocities is considered in building design, floodproofed structures often collapse from the pressures and stresses applied by fast moving water. Water moving at speeds of ten (or more) feet per second can undermine pilings and slab foundations. Water velocity is a major cause of damage in four areas:

-- Areas subject to coastal wave action (velocity zones), coastal inlets and overwash areas;

-- Steep inland floodplain areas along smaller rivers and streams, on alluvial fans, in some riverine floodways, and in mudflow and high gradient sheet flow areas. Steep areas are often flash flood areas with additional damage due to the sudden rise of the water;

-- Areas behind levees or dams where the protective structure suddenly fails or the design capacity is suddenly exceeded;

-- Areas subject to inundation when an ice jam breaks.

Debris in the water. The damage potential of floodwaters may be increased hundreds of times when rapidly flowing floodwaters contain substantial amounts of rock, sediment, ice or other natural or man-made materials. Normal standards for floodproofing and elevation may be inadequate in the following situations:

-- Alluvial fan flood waters, carrying rocks and sediment;

-- Mudflow and mudfloods carrying sediments, rocks, trees and other debris;

-- Meandering streams carrying mud and rocks;

-- Ice jam flood waters carrying ice, rock, trees, parts of structures;

-- High velocity flood waters along rivers and streams carry rocks, sediment, trees, lumber, bridges and other debris;

-- Flood waters from dam or levee failure carrying trees, rocks, lumber and other debris;

-- Coastal waves and storm surges carry rocks, gravel, lumber, and other debris.

Suddenness. Areas subject to rapid inundation by floodwaters or flash floods pose special threats to life and property because there is insufficient time for evacuation, emergency floodproofing or other protective measures. Suddenness is a serious problem in four areas:

-- Steep rivers and streams in mountainous or hilly areas subject to sudden rainfall and rapid runoff;

-- Areas behind dams or levees subject to failure or overtopping;

-- Barrier islands and other areas principally along the Gulf or Atlantic coasts which may be subject to relatively rapid hurricane storm surge; and

-- Coastal areas (principally along the west coast) subject to tsunamis.

Long-term or permanent inundation. Unlike the normal riverine or coastal flood situation where flood waters rise and fall quickly, certain areas are subject to long term or essentially permanent flooding. In such areas, structures elevated on pilings or floodproofed are often permanently unusable and must be abandoned unless they are specially designed for long term inundation with adequate access and utility services. Long term flood areas include:

-- Barrier islands and beaches inundated by rising sea levels;

-- Areas around lakes subject to long-term fluctuations of ground water;

-- Erosion-prone areas such as bluffs, where the land is destroyed;

-- Areas subject to subsidence caused by ground water or oil and gas withdrawals, hydrocompaction or gradual solution of the underlying strata; and

-- Areas behind dikes and levees where high ground water levels may persist for months or years.

Two or more of the special risk factors often occur in combination in high risk areas. For example, high velocity, debris and rapid rise of water combine to cause severe damage on alluvial fans, in ice jam failures, mudflow and areas subject to flooding by the failure of dams or levees. Erosion or blockage of channels by sediment or debris is also common in alluvial fan, mudflow and coastal areas.

CHAPTER 2: COMMUNITY OPTIONS FOR REDUCING FLOOD DAMAGES

Floodplain regulations are the most effective way to reduce future flood losses in high risk areas. They can keep people from locating in the most dangerous areas and require safe building designs for other flood prone areas. But regulations alone cannot deal with all high risk area problems nor can they usually reduce flood damages to existing structures. A variety of measures is often needed.

Regulations. Zoning, subdivision regulations, building codes and other special codes can be used to prohibit or to establish special conditions for development in high risk areas. Conditions include setbacks, additional freeboard or other elevation requirements for building lots, roads, bridges, pipelines and buildings themselves.

Acquisition. Land can be purchased and structures relocated from high risk areas either before a disaster or after buildings have been damaged in a flood. Acquired lands can then be used for public recreation and open space.

Flood warning systems and evacuation plans. Flood warning systems and evacuation plans are critical for areas protected by levees or dams and for areas where flood waters rise suddenly. A system can range from volunteer observers to highly automated equipment. Warning systems and evacuation plans can save lives and may reduce losses to contents of structures.

Engineering measures. Engineering measures have been applied to high risk areas with varying degrees of success. Such measures include groins and bulkheads for coastal erosion areas, debris basins for alluvial fan and mudflow areas, pumping systems for internal drainage behind dikes and levees, the dewatering of mudflood and mudflow areas, and grouting and reinforcement for unsafe dams and levees.

Table 1 presents appropriate flood risk reduction techniques for each of the high risk areas.

STEPS IN REDUCING HIGH RISK FLOOD LOSSES

A comprehensive risk reduction program includes the seven steps described below. If your community has no floodplain management program, or a minimal one, start at step

Table 1: Reducing Flood Losses in High Risk Areas.

Hazard	Special Risk Factors	Area of Occurrence	Management Options
Alluvial Fans	* Lack of permanent drainage channels * Velocity * Sediment and debris * Erosion	Primarily mountainous areas in the west and southwest	* Prohibit development on fans or, if it is to occur, require elevation on pilings or other enclosures to protect against water velocities and debris. * Map fans as high risk areas. * Develop and implement a drainage master plan if development is to occur on fans. * Limit grading, paving, and channelization unless consistent with master plan. * Construct floodwalls, drainage channels, debris basins.
Areas Behind Unsafe or Inadequate Levees	* Velocity * Duration * Suddenness	Riverine areas throughout the country	* Map levees; assess their adequacy. * Define inundation zones for areas behind unsafe or inadequate levees. * Require periodic inspection, maintenance of levees. * Adopt building standards based on risk of breaching or overtopping. * Require pump systems; other methods for dealing with internal drainage behind levees. * Install or require installation of warning systems and evacuation plans for areas protected by unsafe or inadequate levees.
Areas Below Unsafe or Inadequate Dams	* Velocity * Suddenness * Debris in water	Riverine areas throughout the country	* Coordinate floodplain management and dam safety programs. * Map dams; assess their adequacy. * Identify inundation zones for inadequate or unsafe dams as if dams were not in place; map floodway and flood fringe areas. * Abate or require abatement of unsafe or inadequate dams. * Restrict new development below unsafe or inadequate dams.

Table 1, cont.: Reducing Flood Losses in High Risk Areas.

Hazard	Special Risk Factors	Area of Occurrence	Management Options
Areas Below Unsafe or Inadequate Dams, cont.			* Require dam owners to prepare dam inspection schedules and maintenance plans; meet yearly with dam owners to review. * Prepare or require dam owners to prepare warning systems and evacuation plans for areas below unsafe or inadequate dams. * Manage reservoirs to optimize flood hazard reduction.
Coastal Flooding and Erosion	* Structural damage as buildings are undermined * Suddenness * Complete destruction of land (in some instances)	Barrier islands, bluff areas (Great Lakes, West Coast), beaches (Louisiana)	* Gather existing erosion studies and historic data, prepare general or specific maps based upon these or other maps. * Adopt setback lines to prohibit development in erosion prone land and on protective land features such as dunes. * Adopt building performance standards pertaining to depth and specifications for pilings, groins, seawalls, use of septic tanks, surface drainage. * Acquire undeveloped coastline and relocate structures. * Construct groins, seawalls, rebuild beaches and dunes.
Flash Flooding	* Suddenness * Velocity * Debris (often)	Principally mountainous regions in valleys with steep slopes; also urbanizing areas	* Collect historical data on flash flooding; use it and engineering studies to map flash flood inundation areas. * Prohibit development and other activities (e.g. campgrounds) in high risk areas. * Require that new development in other areas be constructed consistent with water velocities and potential debris. * Install or require developers to prepare warning systems; prepare and implement evacuation plans.

Table 1, cont.: Reducing Flood Losses in High Risk Areas.

Hazard	Special Risk Factors	Area of Occurrence	Management Options
Flash Flooding, cont.			* Require that subdividers install onsite flood detention; design drainage systems to reduce flash flood potential. * Mark areas. * Construct reservoirs and other engineering devices to reduce flash floods.
Long-Term Fluctuations in Lake Levels	* Long duration * Waves and ice * Lake quality degradation as flooded sewage systems fail * Ground water quality degradation as flooded wells act as conduit to transfer lake water to aquifers	Primarily northern states (glacially formed lakes) with water elevations dependent upon ground water levels; lakes in western states without outlets	* Map historical bed of lake. * Adopt floodplain, shoreland and wetland ordinances to direct development. * Require elevation of structures and public utilities on fill (not pilings). * Prohibit septic and water systems in flood areas is development is to occur. * Adopt setback back lines or additional freeboard if development is to occur to reduce damage from waves and ice damage to structures. * Acquire flood-prone lands and relocate threatened structures. Install pumps, other engineering works to reduce or stabilize lake levels.
Ground Failure: Liquefaction	* Collapse of structure * Suddenness of flooding	San Francisco Bay, Alaska, New Madrid Fault Zone Area, other areas with saturated soils and earthquake threat	* Conduct special studies to determine areas and levels of risk. * Adopt special building design standards for pilings, densities of development, loading factors. * Acquire highly unstable lands and relocate structures.

Table 1, cont.: Reducing Flood Losses in High Risk Areas.

Hazard	Special Risk Factors	Area of Occurrence	Management Options
Ground Failure: Subsidence	* Structural damage and/or collapse * Permanent inundation * Increasing flood elevations (over time) * Damage to buildings, roads and service lines	Houston/Galveston, New Orleans, Sacramento Delta, and many other areas (localized)	* Prepare maps showing mines, organic soils, karst formations, areas subject to hydrocompaction, etc. * Conduct frequent site inspections and restudies to determine currently expected flood levels and revise 100-year flood protection elevations. * Require pre-development site investigations. * Prohibit development in high risk areas; require adequate foundation support through zoning or building codes in other areas. * Add freeboard to 100-year flood elevations. * Limit ground water, oil & gas withdrawal where it is causing subsidence; computer models can predict subsidence related to amount of withdrawal. * Require reinjection of water in oil & gas drilling operations. * Purchase and relocate structures out of high risk areas.
Ice Jam Flooding	* Unexpected flood levels * Suddenness * High velocity * Debris (ice floes)	Principally 35 northern states including Alaska; jams occur most often at constriction points in river valleys	* Collect historical data on ice jam floods; use it or engineering studies to map ice jam inundation areas. * Adopt setback lines. * Require additional freeboard to protect against ice. * Adopt construction standards, especially for floodproofing, that consider ice damage. * Acquire hazardous lands and relocate structures that cannot be protected. * Develop a warning system and emergency action plan. * Undertake remedial engineering measures.

Table 1, cont.: Reducing Flood Losses in High Risk Areas.

Hazard	Special Risk Factors	Area of Occurrence	Management Options
Mud floods and Mud flows	* Debris. * Velocity (in some instances) * Suddenness	The arid and semi-arid west; Appalachia	* Gather and use available data to map mud flow areas. * Require developers in slope areas with unconsolidated soils to prepare engineering studies. * Prohibit development in high risk areas; require that developments in other areas be constructed on compacted fill or with adequate foundations on pilings to accommodate expected water and debris. * Construct debris basins, retaining walls, other remedial measures.

one and work in order. Communities with ongoing floodplain management efforts may simply need to upgrade existing plans and regulations.

Step One: Set Policy

To begin a high risk area program, your community should evaluate existing plans and regulations and decide whether additional measures are needed. An initial declaration of intent to upgrade existing measures should be the first action. This intent is known as a policy.

Policy expresses your government's commitment to reducing damage from high risk flooding and provides the authority and guidance for mapping, regulation and other activities. Policy can be thought of as an expression of political will. Elected leaders and administrators want to get something done -- in this case save lives and reduce private and public costs of flooding. Policy guidelines establish the form and content of a high risk flood program:

> **Content.** Is it a regulatory program or does it include acquisition, flood warnings or other techniques?

> **Intergovernmental relationships.** Is one agency or office given the lead over others? Is coordination formal or informal?

> **Funding.** Is there a constant allocation from general revenues? Are federal or state grants needed? Can funds be raised from a permit application fee or through special assessments?

Policy can take several forms:

>> -- Proclamations or orders by a chief executive;
>> -- Resolutions of committees or councils;
>> -- Formal statements of agreement between government bodies or agencies;
>> -- Adoption of plans and regulations.

The policy-making process starts whenever any individual or group realizes that there is a public problem and begins to take action. For example, a floodplain manager may realize that sedimentation has decreased the capacity of an upstream reservoir and that the dam could be overtopped. In addition to making sure that the dam is regularly checked for safety, the manager may draft a policy statement for the city council recognizing that the dam is unsafe. The statement may also suggest that the parks, civil defense and planning departments cooperate with a neighborhood advisory council to prepare an evacuation plan. Upon learning the facts, the city governing body could, by resolution, adopt this statement to guide further community action.

This new policy would form the basis for more specific plans or regulations, for enforcing protective laws to their fullest extent and for obtaining funds and other assistance to plan and implement a risk reduction program. An initial declaration of policy will be refined as high risk areas are studied and more detailed plans are made for reducing potential future losses.

Step Two: Assess the General Location and Extent of Hazards

The second step is to identify and evaluate potential high risk areas. Where are the high risk areas in your community? Have there been past flood losses in such areas?

Often considerable public information already exists in the form of flood damage reports, flood records, flood maps, newspaper accounts or other historical data to suggest where high risk flooding has occurred. If damages have not occurred in the area before, the potential risk may be unknown. For example, alluvial fans in the arid west are often not recognized as high risk areas due to lack of recent flood damage. People living half a mile from a small meandering stream may not realize that the stream can change its course rapidly.

Hazard assessments can be conducted by emergency management personnel, planners, city engineers or consultants. Information on hazard assessment is available from the sources listed in the appendices of the individual chapters which follow.

Step Three: Map High Risk Areas

Once the general location of a high risk has been identified, mapping is usually needed to determine the more precise extent of the area affected. Once areas are mapped, regulations and other management measures can be adopted. Maps can be of two types:

1)   *General*, indicating the area where conditions create the potential for damage; or

2)   *Specific*, delineating locations of known frequency and level of flooding.

Generalized maps are useful for initial planning and zoning but often must be supplemented with more detailed onsite investigations when development is proposed.Such a regulatory procedure is incorporated in the single district floodplain zoning ordinance proposed in Volume 1 of *Regulation of Flood Hazard Areas to Reduce Flood Losses*. (U.S. Government Printing Office, 1971 and 1972.) The general map only establishes the regulatory jurisdiction. The specific hazard at a site is determined by case-by-case analysis as individual permit applications are submitted.

Relatively large scale maps (at least 1 inch = 1000 feet) are usually needed for zoning urban high risk areas. Smaller scales may be sufficient for rural settings. A frequency analysis of the hazard is desirable to identify the extent of the 100-year event.

Historical data and other readily available information can be used to identify high risk areas if engineering studies are not available or cannot be undertaken due to time limitations or inadequate budget. Request assistance in mapping from the U.S. Army Corps of Engineers, U.S. Soil Conservation Service, the Federal Emergency Management Agency or the U.S. Geological Survey. Your state floodplain management program may also help.

Step Four: Prepare Plans

A plan provides the background for future public and private decisions which can be made to reduce flood risk. Regulations are one way of implementing plans. Plans and regulations are developed in similar ways, using technical information to apply policies to local conditions.

Plans for reducing flood risk can take several forms:
-- Land use or development plans;
-- Evacuation and other emergency operation plans;
-- Drainage and watershed management plans;
-- Acquisition and/or relocation plans.

The form and content of the plans needed for your community will depend upon the nature and extent of high risk flooding and possible solutions.

Step Five: Prepare and Adopt Regulations

With the exception of some coastal velocity zones and floodways, normal regulations usually underestimate the hazard in high risk areas and therefore do not require adequate protection measures. Amendments or new ordinances are often needed. In some instances, such as ice jam flooding, the protection elevations must be increased. In others, the management approaches must be changed. For example, elevation of structures on pilings does not provide flood protection from long-term lake level fluctuations unless roads and utilities are also elevated and the pilings and structures are designed for permanent or semi-permanent inundation.

On their own initiative or at the urging of the states, several hundred communities have adopted special hazard regulations for alluvial fan, mudflood, coastal erosion and other risk areas. Regulations are usually part of broader zoning, subdivision controls or building codes. Strengthened regulatory approaches for high risk areas may include:

1) Absolute prohibition of development in areas of high risk, where development will substantially increase flood heights or erosion on other lands or where engineering solutions are impractical. Interim prohibitions or moratoria that stop reconstruction are especially appropriate after a disaster.

2) Added elevation requirements through freeboard or increased base elevations to reflect the additional risk (e.g., wave heights, ice jams).

3) Strengthened performance standards to reflect not only water depth but also velocity, debris and other risk factors. Applicants for building permits or subdivision plat approval can be required to undertake hydrologic and geologic investigations to specifically determine the hazards at sites and then to design the proposed structure consistent with the hazards.

Step Six: Implement and Enforce Plans and Regulations

Adoption is only the first step in implementing plans and regulations. Formulation of plans and regulations is primarily a technical effort; the implementation and enforcement which must follow is in part an educational process. Administrators, elected officials, interest group leaders and the general public must be informed of the content of plans and regulations and how they will work. Their support is essential to long-term success.

Step Seven: Incorporating Nonregulatory Approaches

Plans and regulations alone cannot remedy threats to existing structures. A combination of education, public acquisition, financial incentives, warning and evacuation systems, technical assistance and engineering measures is often appropriate to reduce damage from high risk flooding. The appropriate combination will depend upon your community's needs, problems, levels of funding, amount of existing development and other factors.

Use of the recommended sources of information presented in Table 2 will aid in the execution of your flood risk reduction program.

Table 2: Sources of Mapping Assistance.

Type of Hazard	Mapping Methods, Data
Alluvial Fan Flooding	* Topographic maps from U.S. Geological Survey * County Soil Surveys from U.S. Soil Conservation Service (type of sediment) * Aerial photographs - from U.S. Agricultural Stabilization and Conservation Service (locate fan formations) * Map methodology from Federal Emergency Management Agency (See bibliography for other methods.)
Areas Behind Unsafe or Inadequate Levees	* FEMA flood maps * U.S. Soil Conservation Service flood-maps
Areas Below Unsafe or Inadequate Dams	* U.S. Army Corps of Engineers Dam Safety reports * State Dam Safety Reports. * FEMA map feasibility study. * Colorado and California Dam Safety Programs
Coastal Flooding and Erosion	* State maps and a variety of data from state coastal zone management and floodplain management programs, state university sea grant and college programs. * Historic and current maps from the U.S. Geological Survey, U.S. Coast and Geodetic Survey, U.S. Agricultural Stabilization & Conservation Service, state university cartographers.
Flash Flooding	* List of flash-flood prone communities, National Weather Service * FEMA flood maps * State floodplain management agencies U.S. Geological Survey topographic maps * Records of events, damages and hydrologic studies from the U.S. Army Corps of Engineers, Soil Conservation Service, state water re source and floodplain management agencies * Local newspaper archives, long-term residents.
Lake Level Fluctuation	* Historical lake level data from U.S. Geological Survey (topographic maps show lake area) * State agency records (regular lake gauge reading program, special studies in conjunction with permits) * Long-term residents (survey and photographs) * State historical society (land survey records).

Table 2, cont.: Sources of Mapping Assistance.

Type of Hazard	Mapping Methods, Data
Ground Failure: Liquefaction	* General and detailed assessments of earthquake and liquefaction probability from U.S. Geological Survey.
Ground Failure: Subsidence	* Geological studies, water atlas from U.S. Geological Survey karst strata, ground water information) * Soil surveys from U.S. Soil Conservation Service (organic soils). * Mine and irrigation locations from state regulatory agencies. * Historic events and damages from local newspaper archives * Information on karst terrain mapping methods and assistance in studies from Florida Sinkhole Research Institute.
Ice Jam Flooding	* Historical records of ice jam floods from local newspaper archives. * Historical data concerning locations where ice jam floods have occurred from long-term residents * Some flood insurance rate maps from the Federal Emergency Management Agency show ice jam flood-prone areas * Map method from U.S. Army Corps of Engineers Cold Regions Research and Engineering Laboratory (see bibliography)
Mudfloods and Mudflows	* Historical records of events and damages from U.S. or state geological surveys, archives, university geology departments * Topographic maps from U.S. Geological Survey * Soil surveys from U.S. Soil Conservation Service

CHAPTER 3. ALLUVIAL FANS

THE HAZARD

Alluvial fans are fan-shaped deposits of rock and soil which eroded from mountainsides and accumulated on the valley floors. The deposits are narrow and steep at the head of the valley, broadening as they spread out onto the valley floor -- hence the name fans. Rain runs off of steep valley walls, gaining velocity and carrying large boulders and other debris. When the debris fills the runoff channels on the fan, flood waters spill out and cut new channels. The process is then repeated, resulting in shifting channels and combined erosion and flooding problems over a large area.

Flood and erosion problems on fans are often complicated by the activities of man. Roads act as drainage channels, carrying high velocity flows to lower portions of the fan. Fill, leveling, grading and structures can divert waters and cause new and unexpected patterns of flooding and erosion.

Alluvial fans occur principally in dry, mountainous areas. They are common in California, Nevada, Utah, Arizona, Idaho, New Mexico, Wyoming, Montana and Washington. Some fans are also found in Alaska, West Virginia, Kentucky and Tennessee.

Flooding on alluvial fans causes greater damage than clear water flooding for several reasons:

1. Floodwaters move at high velocities due to steep slopes and lack of vegetation. Velocities of 15 to 30 feet per second are common. At these velocities, water has tremendous erosive force and damage potential.

2. Floodwaters contain large amounts of sediment and debris including boulders and trees.

3. Floodwaters are not confined to a single channel. The channels meander, threatening development over a broad area.

EXISTING MITIGATION EFFORTS

Often alluvial fans have been mapped and regulated as shallow flooding areas requiring minimal flood protection through fill or elevation on pilings. These maps and regulations underestimate actual risk on fans because they are based on depth of flooding alone. They do not reflect potential damage due to high velocity, debris, erosion or the meandering channel. Some progress has been made in mapping, regulating and managing fans consistent with their true hazard.

Federal

In 1982, the National Flood Insurance Program (NFIP) commissioned a study of mapping, modeling and land management standards for alluvial fan areas. The study resulted in the development of suggested management standards for these zones on the fan: a channelized zone, a braided zone and a sheet flow zone (see Figure 3-1, Appendix 3-A). In addition to this study, the NFIP has promulgated mapping guidelines for flood insurance study contractors (see Appendix 3-B). FEMA's Region X has also drafted a model ordinance for communities with alluvial fan flood problems (see Appendix 3-C). This has been presented to several communities.

The U.S. Geological Survey and the Corps of Engineers have also mapped some alluvial fan areas and are working on alluvial fan mapping methods.

State

State efforts to develop special maps and regulations for alluvial fans have been limited, although Colorado has recommended to local governments a model ordinance addressing fans and other geological hazard areas (see Appendix 3-D).

California's geologic hazard investigation and reporting system requires local governments to identify and regulate geologic hazard areas. This requirement applies to some types of hazards on the fans. Developers seeking a building permit or subdivision approval for projects on fans must have a certified geologist prepare a geologic report assuring the risk.

Nevada has developed an alluvial fan management handbook for local governments but has not adopted regulatory requirements.

Local

Most of the innovative efforts to map, regulate and otherwise manage alluvial fans have occurred at the local level.

Riverside County, California, has developed an alluvial fan methodology and mapped alluvial fans in the Cabazon area. It has also adopted special regulations reflecting flood velocities, erosive force and debris.

Los Angeles County, California has mapped alluvial fans and adopted a grading code for these and other areas.

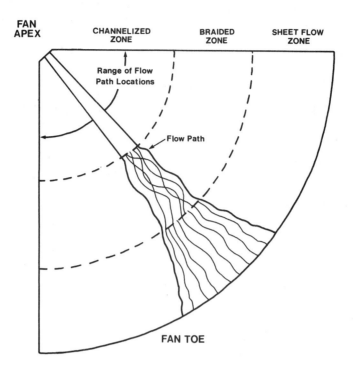

Figure 3-1. Hydraulic zones on a typical fan.   Source: FEMA.

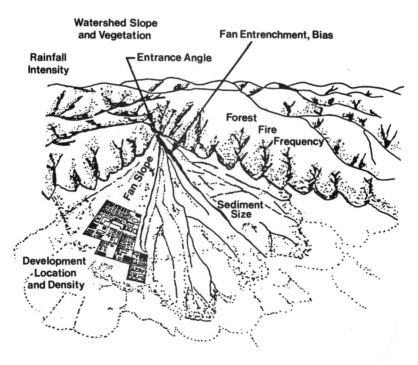

Figure 3-2. Factors affecting flood hazards on alluvial fans.

Wenachee, Washington, mapped alluvial fan areas and adopted special regulations The maps were later sustained in court (see Figure 3-3).

Rancho Mirage, Whittier, Palm Desert, and Palm Springs, California have adopted alluvial fan regulations.

Clark County, Nevada and the City of Las Vegas have adopted a master plan for an alluvial fan system and regulations to implement the plan.

OPTIONS FOR COMMUNITY ACTION

Policy and Program Elements

A community with alluvial fan flooding should adopt a policy and program which contains the following elements:

1. A statement that alluvial fans are much more hazardous than shallow flooding areas or normal riverine floodplains due to the combined erosion and flooding problem;

2. A mapping program, perhaps as an overlay system for existing land use base maps;

3. Special standards for siting and constructing on fan areas to address velocity, debris and erosion;

4. A master drainage and development plan for the fan as a whole, including careful design and siting of roads, drainageways and other public works on the fan;

5. Construction of debris basins or other engineering measures for the fan, particularly where existing development is at risk.

Mapping

At a minimum, alluvial fan areas should be identified on flood maps as high risk areas. Some alluvial fans have already been identified on flood insurance study maps as "shallow flooding" areas. Fans so designated should either be remapped or an overlay map should be prepared to indicate areas where water velocities, debris, erosion and channel migration are potential problems.

It may be possible to identify alluvial fan areas at modest cost using existing air photos, soils maps and topographic data. Alluvial fans are often highly visible in arid and semi-arid areas due to their distinctive shape and the presence of boulder trains. In

Figure 3-3. Topographic characteristics of typical alluvial fans and alluvial aprons (Wenatchee, Washington).   Source: FEMA.

Figure 3-4. Trailer park built on alluvial fan.   Source: R. Platt.

forested areas, fans may be more difficult to map. Topographic and soils maps may be used to identify areas with steep slopes and alluvium.

An outline of alluvial fan areas can, even without more detailed identification of risk zones within the fans, be an important "red flag" for land use decisions. Once outlined, fans can be zoned as high risk areas. Developers can be required to conduct detailed studies of the flood risk and design accordingly.

Engineering methods, although quite expensive, are available for mapping fans in more detail and determining the relative risks within the fans. With these maps, zoning regulation can be quite specific. However, site-specific studies and master planning will still be needed as new development is proposed.

Regulations

Regulations for alluvial systems should have two principal goals: to prevent acceleration or diversion of runoff and increased erosion, and to insure that individual structures and infrastructures are adequately protected from high velocity flows, debris and erosion.

If the fan is undeveloped, future flood damages can be avoided by prohibiting development. Development should only be permitted if a master plan has been prepared. An alluvial fan master plan should show the drainage system, roads, grading and filling needed for drainageways, debris walls and other flood protective measures, such as bank stabilization, erosion control measures and floodways to be maintained as open space. Where the fan is in multiple ownership, the community should prepare the master plan. Developers can be required to implement their portion as a condition of plat approval or building permits. Las Vegas takes this approach. Where the fan is in single ownership, regulations may require the developer to prepare a master plan for the fan as a whole. Zoning, subdivision controls or grading codes can be adopted to limit development densities, impervious surfaces and modifications to natural topography.

To help protect individual structures, include the following provisions in your building codes, zoning regulations, grading codes and subdivision regulations:

1. Prohibit building in areas where velocities exceed a selected threshold level (e.g., 7 feet per second).

2. Require that structures in other areas be elevated on stabilized fill or reinforced pilings to a height above the 100-year flood elevation, taking into account debris as well as water elevations.

3.   Require pilings below scour depth (see Figure 3-5).

4.   Require slope protection for fill.

5.   Require that fill be provided not only for individual structures but also for roads and public utilities since much of the damage due to alluvial fan flooding is to infrastructure.

Non-Regulatory Approaches

Regulations should be combined with non-regulatory options depending upon the levels of existing development (see Figure 3-6). Two of the principal non-regulatory approaches for reducing losses on fans are to acquire fans or portions of fans and to construct debris basins and other engineering works to stabilize the drainage pattern on the fan and reduce erosion as well as flooding.

<u>Acquisition</u>

Fans may be kept in an undeveloped condition through public purchase rather than regulation. Fans can be used as parks, recreation areas or open space where public access is desirable. Such an approach is expensive but avoids constitutional problems and allows active public use of the fan.

<u>Debris Basins</u>

Dams may be constructed on the upper portion of fans or along drainage channels to collect sediment, rocks and floodwaters. Such dams and the resulting debris basin are effective in temporarily stopping debris flows but are expensive and must be periodically emptied. Disposal of a large amount of debris is a major problem. The cities of Los Angeles and San Diego have constructed debris basins.

<u>Floodwalls, Channels, Other Engineering Works</u>

A variety of engineering works such as flood walls and concrete channels can help prevent channel migration and accommodate runoff. If any engineering works are to be constructed on a fan, a master plan for development and drainage should be prepared. The location and design of roads must be part of such a plan since roads often block or convey flood waters.

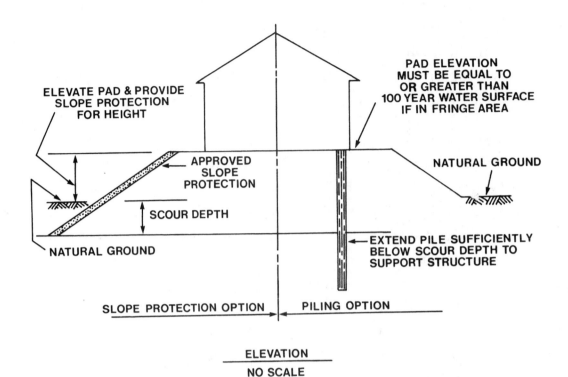

ELEVATE PAD & PROVIDE
SLOPE PROTECTION
FOR HEIGHT

PAD ELEVATION
MUST BE EQUAL TO
OR GREATER THAN
100 YEAR WATER SURFACE
IF IN FRINGE AREA

APPROVED
SLOPE
PROTECTION

NATURAL GROUND

SCOUR DEPTH

NATURAL GROUND

EXTEND PILE SUFFICIENTLY
BELOW SCOUR DEPTH TO
SUPPORT STRUCTURE

SLOPE PROTECTION OPTION   PILING OPTION

ELEVATION

NO SCALE

Figure 3-5: Suggested floodproofing criteria for structure in alluvial fan area.   Source: Riverside County Flood Control and Water Conservation District's Cabazon Flood Study.

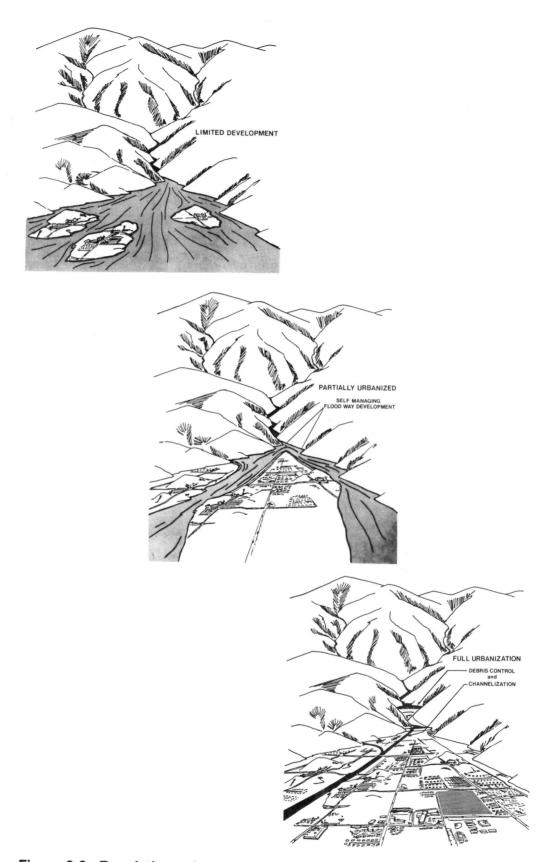

LIMITED DEVELOPMENT

PARTIALLY URBANIZED

SELF MANAGING
FLOOD WAY DEVELOPMENT

FULL URBANIZATION

DEBRIS CONTROL
and
CHANNELIZATION

Figure 3-6: Regulations should be combined with nonregulatory options depending upon the levels of existing development.

Appendix 3-A: Suggested Development Guidelines for Various Hydraulic Zones on the Fan.

The following applications of management tools were recommended by *Floodplain Management Tools for Alluvial Fans*, a report prepared for the Federal Emergency Management Agency (1981). The recommendations apply to each hydraulic zone on the fan and for the placement of single structures:

Channelized Zone
Development prohibited unless whole-fan measures are implemented.

Braided Zone
Basements and mobile homes prohibited.

Streets aligned and designed to convey entire flood flow.

Use of local dikes to direct flows into streets.

Use of drop structures between homes built on high slopes to prevent excessive erosion.

All management tools must be coordinated with tools in existing developments.

Whole-fan management tools can be used instead of the above provisions.

Shallow Flooding Zone
Elevation of structures on piles or armored fill.

Street orientation to maximize flood conveyance.

If up-fan subdivisions use depressed streets or channels to convey floods, these tools must be continued down to the fan toe.

Use of drop structures between homes built on high slopes.

Whole-fan management tools can be used instead of the above provisions.

Placement of Single Structures
In undeveloped areas, place structures on armored fill or use local dikes provided that no added flood damage to other structures results.

In developed areas, local dikes, channels and armored fill must tie in with existing flood control tools.

Elevation on piles should be used if above criteria cannot be met.

No single placement should be allowed in the channelized zone.

Appendix 3-B: FEMA's Guidelines for Study Contractors: Alluvial Fan Studies

From *Guidelines and Specifications for Contractors,* September 1982, FEMA - 37/July 83 printing, Federal Emergency Management Agency, Washington, D.C.

1. INTRODUCTION

The methodology outlined in this Appendix is based on procedures developed by Dawdy (Reference 1) and later modified (Reference 2) to account for split flow conditions generally found in the lower reaches of active alluvial fans. It is recommended that the Study Contractor review these publications for a complete discussion of the theory, rationale and assumptions used to develop this methodology. In portions of alluvial fans in which natural alluvial fan processes may not occur, such as in areas of entrenched channels, areas protected by flood control works, and heavily developed areas, the Study Contractor should exercise good engineering judgment in determining the most appropriate methodology or combinations of methodologies.

When it is determined that an area in a community is subject to alluvial fan flooding, a thorough reconnaissance of the alluvial fan should be made in order to determine the source of flooding, the apex of the fan, the boundaries the fan, the areas of coalescence of contiguous fans, the limits of entrenched channels, single and multiple channel regions where evident, and the areas of active alluvial fan processes. The reconnaissance should make use of available topographic, geologic, and soil maps; aerial photographs; historic records; and site inspection.

Prior to undertaking any computations, the Study Contractor should obtain approval from the PO for the use of the methodology outlined in this Appendix.

2. ASSUMPTIONS AND OBSERVATIONS

The approach outlined in this Appendix makes use of statistical analyses that relate the probability of given discharges at the apex of a fan to the probability of certain depths and velocity of flow occurring at any point on the fan below the apex. The methodology presented in this Appendix is based on assumptions and observations regarding floodflows on active alluvial fans outlined in the following sections.

a. Channel Pattern and Location

At the time of maximum flow during a major flood event on an active fan, flow does not spread evenly over the fan but is confined to only a portion of the fan surface that carries the water from the apex to the toe of the fan. In upper region of the fan, flood flows are confined to a single channel which is formed by the flow itself through erosion of the loose material that makes up the fan. Because of the relatively steep slopes in the upper region, flood flows are at critical depth and critical velocity. Below the apex of fan (or the zone of entrenchment in the case of mature fans), the channel will occur at random locations at any place on the fan surface; under natural conditions, it is no more likely to follow a pre-existing flowpath than it is to follow a new flowpath. This channel has an approximately rectangular cross section for which depth, width, and velocity of flow can be expressed as functions of discharge at the apex of the fan.

In the lower region of the fan, flood flows split and form multiple channels. For purposes of this procedure, the concept of a single eguivalent channel is used to compute flood depths and velocities. Normal flow conditions are considered to exist in the multiple channel region due to the relatively flatter slopes.

The probability of a point being flooded in a given flood event decreases from the apex to the toe of the fan because the downslope widening of the fan surface provides a greater area over which a channel of given width may occur.

b. Depth of Flooding

For flood mapping purposes, the depth of flooding computed on alluvial fans is the depth of flow (depth of channel) in the channel that carries a given discharge to the toe of the fan surface.

c. Velocity of Flooding

For alluvial fan flood mapping, the velocity of flooding computed for alluvial fan flood mapping is the velocity of flow in the channel that carries the given discharge to the toe of the fan surface.

d. Avulsions

During major floods on active alluvial fans, peak flows may abruptly abandon one channel that had been formed during the flood, and form a new channel This phenomenon, termed an avulsion, can cause a significant increase in the probability of flooding at a given point on a fan because of the increased channel widths that may cross a given contour during a given flood event. The treatment of avulsions is an important factor in the application of the methodology presented in this Appendix.

3. FLOOD HAZARD ZONES

Special flood Hazard Areas on alluvial fans are identified as Zone AO with the following definition:

*Zone AO: Zone AO is the flood insurance rate zone that corresponds to the areas of 100-year shallow flooding (usually sheet flow on sloping terrain) where average depths are between 1 and 3 feet. Average whole-foot depths derived from the detailed hydraulic analyses are shown within this zone.

* *Exception to the 3-foot depth limit for zone AO is permitted for alluvial fans when approved by the PO.*

The Special Flood Hazard Area on each alluvial fan is subdivided into separate AO zones with similar depths and velocities. Zones are delineated that have depths or velocities differing by an average of 1.0 foot in depth or 1.0 foot per second (fps) in velocity.

In areas of coalescent alluvial fans, separate depth-frequency relationships should be developed for each source of flooding and combined based on the probability of the union of independent events.

4. COMPUTATIONAL INSTRUCTIONS

Step-by-step instructions are provided below for computing the boundaries of flood hazard zones on alluvial fans using log-Pearson Type III analyses in accordance with Bulletin No. 17B (Reference 3).

a. Determine Flood Discharge-Frequency Distribution

For the source of flooding at the apex of each alluvial fan, a complete flood discharge-frequency distribution should be determined using log-Pearson Type III analyses in accordance with Bulletin No. 17B. The determination of flood discharges in arid regions, where alluvial fans are most frequently found, should be closely coordinated with the PO to ensure agreement on methodology.

The skew coefficient, standard deviation, and mean of logarithms of discharges must be determined for the flooding source at the apex of the fan. When an analysis according to Bulletin No. 17B is done, these statistics are known. For most alluvial fans, however, these statistics will not be available. Therefore, flows of various recurrence intervals should be computed from appropiate regional methods, and the synthetic log-Pearson Type III parameters should be derived.

Derivation of Skew Coefficient. Derive the skew coefficient using the ollowing equations:

$$G = -2.50 + 3.12 \, \text{Log} \, [(Q_{.01}/_{.10})/(Q_{.10}/_{.50})] \quad (1)$$

Using the skew coefficient computed above and the K values for the skew as shown in Bulletin No. 17B, the standard deviation should be derived according to the following equations:

$$S = [\text{Log}(Q_{.01}/_{.50})/(K_{.01} - K_{.50})] \quad (2)$$

(2) Derivation of Mean of Logarithms. Using the values determined in Equations 1 and 2, the mean of logarithms should be derived according to the following equation:

$$X = \log (Q_{.50}) - K_{.50}(S) \quad (3)$$

where S and X are the standard deviation and mean respectively; $Q_{.01}$, $Q_{.10}$, and $Q_{.50}$ are discharges with 0.01, 0.10 and 0.50 exceedance probabilities; and $K_{.01}$ and $K_{.50}$ are Pearson Type III deviates for respective exceedance probabilities of 0.01 and 0.50 and skew coefficient G. Equation (1) above is an approximation appropriate for use between skew values of +2.5 and -2.0.

b. Compute Transformation Variables

To permit solutions by use of log-Pearson Type III analysis and Bulletin No. 17B, the log-Pearson Type III parameters must be transformed.

Variables for transforming these parameters should be computed as follows:

$$m = \overline{X} - 2S/G$$

$$\text{alpha} = 2/GS$$

$$\text{lambda} = 4/G^2$$

and

$$a = \text{alpha} - 0.92$$

If the skew coefficient is zero (log normal distribution), the transformation variables should not be computed.

c. Transform log-Pearson Type III Parameters

Where skew coefficients are not zero, the log-Pearson Type III parameters should be transformed using the variables above according to the following equations:

$$\overline{Z} = m + \text{lambda}/a$$

$$S_Z^2 = 2/\text{lambda}^{1/2}$$

Where the skew coefficient is zero (log normal distribution), compute the parameters as follows:

$$\overline{Z} = \overline{X} + 0.92S^2$$

$$S_Z = S$$

$$G_Z = G$$

d. Compute Transformation Constant

$$C = (\text{alpha}/a)\text{lambda} \, e^{0.92m}$$

Where the skew coefficient is zero (log normal distribution), the transformation constant should be computed as follows:

$$C = e^{0.92X + 0.42S*S}$$

e. Determine Discharges for Depth and Velocity Zones

The alluvial fan flooding can be determined by a combination of two methods. They are based on a single channel region and a multiple channel region in the analyses. The single channel region is defined by the length of the single channel measured from the mouth of the canyon to the point where the flood channel splits. If there is no clear indication as to the length of the single channel from data collected during the reconnaisance phase, the length of the single channel can be determined using Figure B-1. Below the single channel region of the fan is the multiple channel region. The fan width along the boundary between the single channel and multiple channel regions can be measured from the topographic map, once the length of the single channel is known.

I. Single Channel Region

Within this region, discharges, Q (in cubic feet per second), that correspond to the various depth zone boundaries should be selected using the table below. This table was derived from the relationship:

$$Q = 280 D^{2.5}$$

where D is the total depth in feet due to pressure head and velocity head.

Q	49.5	772	2770	6420	12000
D	0.5	1.5	2.5	3.5	4.5

Depth zones are designated from zone boundaries as follows:

Depth of Zone	Depth of Lower Boundary	Depth of Upper Boundary
1	0.5	1.5
2	1.5	2.5
3	2.5	3.5
4	3.5	4.5

Discharges, Q (in cubic feet per second), that correspond to the various velocity zone boundaries should be selected using the table below. This table was derived from the relationship:

$$Q = 0.13 V^5$$

where V is velocity in feet per second.

Q	68	240	654	1510	3080	5770
V	3.5	4.5	5.5	6.5	7.5	8.5

Velocity zones are designated from zone boundaries as follows:

Zone Velocity	Velocity of Lower Boundary	Velocity of Upper Boundary
4.0	3.5	4.5
5.0	4.5	5.5
6.0	5.5	6.5
7.0	6.5	7.5
8.0	7.5	8.5

II. Multiple Channel Region

Within the multiple channel region, discharges, Q (in cubic feet per second), that correspond to the various depth zone boudaries may be calculated by iteratively solving the following equation:

$$D = 0.0917 \, n^{.6} S^{-.3} Q^{.36} + 0.001426 \, n^{1.2} S^{.6} Q^{.48}$$

where D is the total depth in feet due to pressure head and velocity head, S is the fan slope, and n is Manning's roughness coefficient for the alluvial fan flood channel.

Discharges, Q (in cubic feet per second), that correspon to the various velocity zone boundaries should be calculated using the equation:

$$Q = 99314 \, n^{4.17} S^{-1.25} V^{4.17}$$

where V is velocity in feet per second and S is the fan slope.

Depth zones and velocity are designated from zone boundaries in the same manner as shown in the analysis for the single channel region.

f. Compute Fan Widths for Zone Boundaries

The fan widths (i.e., arc lengths from one lateral limit of the fan to the other taken parallel to contours) that correspond to each upper and lower zone boundary depth and velocity listed in Section 4e should be computed both for the single channel region and the multiple channel region. The following formulas should be used:

I. Single Channel Region

Fan Width = 950ACP

II. Multiple Channel Region

Fan Width = 3610ACP

In the above two formulas, A is the avulsion coefficient, C is the transformation constant, and P is the probability of the discharge that corresponds to each given depth and velocity.

An avulsion coefficient (factor) greater than 1 should be selected by the Study Contractor in consultation with the PO. A factor of 1.5 is recommended in the absence of other data.

In summary, the steps for the determination of the flood velocity and depth boundaries are listed as follows:

1. Compute all flood depth and velocity zone boundaries by the standard single channel method.

2. Determine point of bifurcation into multiple channel region through use of Figure B-1 and the calculation of near fanhead canyon slope to fan slope ratio.

3. If the point of bifurcation is downfan from the lower boundary of the one-foot depth zone as computed by the standard single channel method, the standard single channel method will be used for the determination of all flood boundaries on the fan.

4. If the point of bifurcation is upfan from the upper boundary of the one-foot depth zone as computed by the standard single channel method, the one-foot depth zone boundaries will be changed to that computed for the multiple channel method. Substitute those boundaries for the boundaries computed by the standard single channel method.

5. If the point of bifurcation is upfan from the one-foot depth zone boundaries as computed by the standard single channel method, compute the depth and velocity at the point of bifurcation by the standard single channel method. Compute the velocity and depth boundaries for velocities and depth less than those determined for the point of bifurcation by use of the multiple channel method. Substitute those boundaries for the boundaries computed by the standard single channel method.

5. FIRM

When the fan arc widths that form flood hazard zone boundaries have been computed, these distances should be scaled onto topographic base maps, taking care to make the boundaries parallel to contours.

The sketch map shown in Figure B-1 depicts the typical distribution of flood insurance rate zones on an active alluvial fan, as determined by the methodology outlined in this Appendix.

6. REFERENCES

1. David R. Dawdy, Flood Frequency Estimates on Alluvial Fans, *Journal of the Hydraulics Division, ASCE, Proceedings*, Vol. 105, No. HYII, pp.1407-1413, 1979.

2. DMA Consulting Engineers for FEMA, *Alluvial Fan Flooding Methodology - An Analysis*, August 1985.

3. U.S. Department of the Interior, Interagency Advisory Committee on Water Data, Office of Water Data Coordination, Hydrology Subcommittee, Bulletin No 17B, *Guidelines for Determining Flood Flow Frequency*, September 1981, revised March 1982.

Appendix 3-C: Excerpts from Sample Flood Damage Prevention Ordinance, Prepared by FEMA, Region X, Bothell, Washington.

5.2 STANDARDS FOR ALLUVIAL FANS

Areas subject to alluvial fan flooding have irregular flow paths that result in erosion of existing channels and the undermining of fill material. Those areas are identified on the Flood Insurance Rate Map as AO Zones with velocities.

1. All structures must be securely anchored to minimize the impact of the flood and sediment damage.

2. All new construction and substantial improvements must be elevated on pilings, columns, or armoured fill so that the bottom lowest floor beam is elevated at or above the depth number.

3. Use of all fill materials must be armoured to protect the material from the velocity of the flood flow.

4. All proposals for subdivision development must provide a mitigation plan that identifies the engineering methods used to:

    a. Protect structures from erosion and scour caused by the velocity of the flood flow.

    b. Capture or transport flood and sediment flow through the subdivision to a safe point of deposition.

5. All mobile homes shall be prohibited within the identified hazard area except within existing mobile home parks or subdivisions.

Appendix 3-D: Excerpts from Colorado's Model Geologic Hazard Area Control Regulations.

The following model regulations for identification, designation, and control of land use in areas of geologic hazard were prepared by the Colorado Geological Survey in accordance with statutory charges contained in Colorado HB-1041. Whereas, at least to our knowledge, comparable laws or regulations dealing with geologic hazard areas have never been written, this has been a pioneer effort. However, since laws, regulations, and administrative procedures for floodplain hazard areas have been developed and tested during the past, they have drawn heavily upon the language of tested floodplain regulations in drafting these model regulations.

WHEREAS, authority for the governing body of a municipality or a county to adopt, amend, repeal, enforce and otherwise administer under the police power reasonable Geologic Hazard Area Land Use Control Regulations and orders pertaining to land use within the areas of its jurisdiction..., and

WHEREAS, the uncontrolled use of land within geologic hazard areas...adversely affects the public health, safety and welfare of the citizens..., and

WHEREAS, the governing body...is empowered...to designate and administer areas of state interest in a manner that will minimize significant hazards to public health and safety or to property due to a geologic hazard, and

WHEREAS, geologic hazards are declared to be matters of state interest and are defined...to include but not be limited to avalanches, landslides, rockfalls, mud flows, unstable or potentially unstable slopes, seismic effects, radioactivity and ground subsidence;

...NOW, THEREFORE, the Board of County Commissioners (City Council) does enact the following Geologic Hazard Area Control Regulation:

SECTION 1.0 PURPOSES

To promote the public health, safety and general welfare, to minimize the effect of significant hazards to public health and safety or to property due to a geologic hazard by the proper administration of all land use changes within such geologic hazard areas, and to promote wise use of geologic hazard areas. This Geologic Area Control Regulation has been established with the following purposes intended:

1.1   To reduce the impact of geologic hazards to life and property by:

    1.11   Prohibiting certain land uses...

    1.12   Restricting the uses which would be hazardous...

    1.13   Restricting the uses which are particularly vulnerable to geologic hazards so as to alleviate hardship and reduce the demands for public expenditures for relief and protection.

    1.14   Restricting permitted land uses in geologic hazard areas, including public facilities...to be protected...by providing for geologic hazard investigation and avoidance or mitigation or hazard impacts at the time of construction.

1.15   Adopting Chapter 70 of the Uniform Building Code...for the regulation of excavation and grading of lands...

1.2   To protect geologic hazard area occupants or users from the impacts of geologic hazards which may be caused by their own, or other, land use and which is or may be undertaken without full realization of the danger by:

    1.21   Regulating the area in which, or the manner in which, structures designed for human occupancy may be constructed...

    1.22   Designating, delineating and describing areas that could be adversely affected by geologic hazards so as to protect individuals from purchasing or improperly utilizing lands for purposes which are not suited.

1.3   To protect the public from the burden of excessive financial expenditures from the impacts of geologic hazard and relief by:

    1.31   Regulating land uses within geologic hazard areas so as to produce a pattern of development or a soundly engineered manner of construction which will minimize the intensity and/or probability of damage to property and loss of life...

    1.32   Regulating the cutting, filling, or drainage changes...which could initiate or intensify adverse conditions within geologic hazard areas.

SECTION 2.0 GENERAL PROVISIONS

2.1   Jurisdiction: This regulation is applicable to all lands within Designated Geologic Hazard Areas...

2.2   Boundaries: The boundaries of the Designated Geologic Hazard Areas shall be as they appear on the official recorded Designated Geologic Hazard Area Maps as adopted... and kept on file...

2.3   Interpretation: In their interpretation and application, the provision ... shall be held to be minimum requirements and shall be liberally construed in favor of the governing body... Interpretations... shall be consistent with GUIDELINES AND CRITERIA FOR GEOLOGIC HAZARD AREAS prepared by the Colorado Geological Survey...

2.4   Warning and Disclaimer of Liability: The degree of protection from geologic hazards intended to be provided by this Regulation is considered reasonable for regulatory purposes, and is based on accepted geologic and scientific methods of study...unforeseen or unknown geologic conditions or natural or man-made changes in conditions such as climate, ground water, drainage, or structural strengths of the rocks and other geologic materials may contribute to future damages to structures and land uses even though properly permitted...

2.5   Adoption of Official Maps: The location and boundaries of the Designated Geologic Hazard Areas established by this Regulation are shown upon the official Designated Geologic Hazard Area Maps...which are hereby incorporated into this Regulation...

SECTION 3.0 NONCONFORMING USES.

SECTION 4.0 DESIGNATED GEOLOGIC HAZARD AREAS.

4.1 Application

4.2 Description of Designated Geologic Hazard Areas

4.3 Description of Permitted Uses: The following open uses shall be permitted within Designated Geologic Hazard Areas...

    4.31 Agricultural uses such as general farming, grazing, truck farming, forestry, sod farming and wild crop harvesting;

    4.32 Industrial-commercial uses such as loading areas, parking areas...and storage yards for equipment...easily moved or not subject to geologic hazard damage.

    4.33 Public and private recreational uses not requiring permanent structures designed for human habitation...if such uses do not cause concentrations of people in areas during periods of high hazard probability.

SECTION 5.0 ADMINISTRATION

5.1 Designated Geologic Hazard Area Administrator...

5.2 Application for Development Permit...

5.3 Permit Review...

5.4 Permit Approval or Denial...

5.5 Mapping Disputes...

SECTION 6.0 ENFORCEMENT AND PENALTIES

SECTION 7.0 AMENDMENTS

SECTION 8.0 SEVERABILITY

SECTION 9.0 DEFINITIONS

SELECTED REFERENCES ON ALLUVIAL FAN FLOODING

California Department of Water Resources, 1980, *California Flood Management: An Evaluation of Flood Damage Prevention Programs.* Bulletin 199. Sacramento: Dept. of Water Resources.

Committee On Natural Disasters, Natural Research Council, and Environmental Quality Laboratory, California Institute of Technology. *Storms, Floods and Debris Flows in Southern California and Arizona--1978 and 1980.* Proceedings of a Symposium, September 17-18, 1980. Washington, D.C.: National Academy of Sciences.

Dawdy, D.R., 1979, *Flood Frequency Estimates on Alluvial Fans.* Journal of Hydraulics Division, A.S.C.E. 105 (HY11)

Douglas, J.R., D.T. Larson, D.H. Hoggan, and T.F. Glover, 1980, *Floodplain Management Needs Peculiar to Arid Climates.* Water Resources Bulletin 16: 1020-1029.

Edwards, K.L. and J. Thielman, 1982, *Flood Plain Management Cabazon, California.* American Society of Civil Engineers Meeting, April 26-30, 1982.

Federal Emergency Management Agency, 1982, *Methodology for Analysis of Flood Hazards on Alluvial Fans.* Washington, D.C.: FEMA.

-----, 1985, *Guidelines and Specifications for Flood Insurance Study Contractors.* Washington, D.C.: FEMA.

Hays, W. (editor), 1981, *Facing Geologic and Hydrologic Hazards: Earth-Science Considerations.* Geological Survey Professional Paper 1240-B. Washington, D.C.: U.S. Government Printing Office.

Magura, L.M. and D.E. Wood, 1980, *Flood Hazard Identification and Flood Plain Management on Alluvial Fans.* Water Resources Bulletin 16: 56-62.

Planning Research Company, 1980, *Cabazon Flood Study. A Report on Flooding from San Gorgino River, Jenson Creek and Millard Canyon Creek.* Riverside, California: Riverside County Flood Control District.

Roberts, B.R., E.W. Shanahan, Y.H. Chen, A.A. Fiuzat and H.J. Owen, 1981, *Flood Plain Management Tools for Alluvial Fans.* Final Report to the Federal Emergency Management Agency. Palo Alto, California: Anderson-Nichols & Company.

Rodgers, W.P., L.R. Ludwig, A.L. Hornbarker, S.D. Schwochow, S.S. Hart, D.C. Shelton, D.L. Scroggs and J.M. Saule, no date, *Guidelines and Criteria for Identification and Land Use Controls of Geologic Hazard and Mineral Resources Areas.* Denver, Colorado: Colorado Geological Survey.

Scullin, C.M., 1983, *Excavation and Grading Code Administration, Inspection and Enforcement*. Englewood Cliffs, New Jersey: Prentice Hall.

Tettemer, J.M., no date, *Angel Park: Keystone of a Master Plan on an Alluvial Cone*. Unpublished paper. Los Angeles, California: John M. Tettemer & Associates.

U.S. Geological Survey, 1981, *Goals, Strategies, Priorities and Tasks of a National Landslide Hazard-Reduction Program*. Open File Report 81-987. Washington, D.C.: USGS.

U.S. Geological Survey, 1982, *Goals and Tasks of the Landslide Part of a Ground Failure Hazard Reduction Program*. Circular No. 880. Menlo Park, California: USGS.

CHAPTER 4: AREAS BEHIND UNSAFE OR INADEQUATE LEVEES

THE HAZARD

An estimated 25,000 miles of levees have been built nationwide. Levees are the most common type of flood control works. They do reduce flood losses. However, results of the U.S. Army Corps of Engineers non-federal dam inspection program suggest that a large percentage of private or locally built levees provide a low level of protection or are poorly designed and maintained. Some privately-built levees may have had no design standards at all. Over time, a levee's history -- and the limitations on its protective capability -- are easily forgotten. Levee overtopping or failure is involved in approximately one-third of all flood disasters.

Levees provide only partial protection from flood problems for several reasons:

1. Many levees (emergency, agricultural) are designed to provide protection only from smaller floods (e.g., 5-15 year flood frequencies) or a specific flood event.

2. Only a portion of all earthen levees built with crown elevations at the computed 100-year flood elevation can provide the expected protection because of changing hydrologic conditions and the possibility of structural failure before overtopping.

3. Areas behind levees are often subject to severe internal drainage problems. The exclusion of flood waters also serves to retain stormwater runoff. Surfacing ground water may be another problem. For example, containment of the Colorado River flows within the levee has resulted in high water table levels along hundreds of miles of levees in Arizona. This high water table has damaged crops and municipal facilities, including sewer and water supply lines and streets, although there is no direct river flooding.

Figure 4-1. Levees run the gamut from carefully designed and built structures to haphazard devices of unknown protective capability.   Source: unknown.

Types of Levees

Flood Control Levees

During the last three decades, the U.S. Army Corps of Engineers, the U.S. Department of Agriculture Soil Conservation Service, the U.S. Bureau of Reclamation and the Tennessee Valley Authority have designed and constructed flood control levees. Most major federal levees are structurally sound, but levels of protection and maintenance vary. Their integrity may also be threatened by changing hydrologic conditions.

Emergency Levees

In 1969, Congress authorized the U.S. Army Corps of Engineers to construct emergency levees, in cooperation with states and local governments. When flooding is imminent, the Corps will construct emergency protective devices if the community agrees to

1. provide rights of way,
2. provide common labor,
3. supply fill,
4. retain responsibility for damages.

Theoretically, the community must also remove the levee and dispose of materials. This last requirement, removal of all emergency levees, has not been steadfastly enforced. As a result, many miles of unsafe levees now exist.

Agricultural Levees

Earthen agricultural levees are typically constructed to protect cropland from frequent floods. While their failure may not cause significant property damage as long as structures are not built behind them, agricultural levees may contribute to risks. Often built at the edge of the channel by the landowner and without adequate technical analysis, agricultural levees can increase flood velocities or elevations upstream, downstream or on adjacent lands. In addition, if the farmland is later developed, local communities and landowners will tend to assume that the levees provide a larger degree of flood protection than they do.

Other Locally Constructed Levees

Independently constructed levees are often built by communities or individuals after a history of frequent flooding Various design standards and construction materials have been used. It is rarely possible to determine the structural adequacy of these levees without an extensive evaluation.

Areas behind levees may be at risk of greater than normal flood damage for several reasons. Floodplain residents believe that they are protected from floods and do not feel it necessary to take proper precautions. A levee breach, like a dam break, unleashes flood waters with very high velocity. After a breach, the downstream portion of levee system may also act as a dam, prolonging the flooding behind it.

EXISTING MITIGATION EFFORTS

Efforts to control development behind levees have been limited. The National Flood Insurance Program has established minimum standards for levees (see Appendix 4-A). Buildings behind substandard levees pay insurance rates as if the levee did not exist. Several states also regulate lands behind inadequate levees as if such levees do not exist.

Levees -- A Curse or a Blessing?

The story of the Santa Cruz Flood Control Project

The San Lorenzo River drains approximately 140 square miles in the Central California Coast Range. Most of the drainage basin is covered with dense redwood forest. Steep slopes are common in the upper portion of the watershed. Widespread occurrence of unstable soils in much of the watershed and an average 47 inches annual rainfall cause landslides and severe erosion in certain parts of the basin. Intense logging, quarrying and other activities associated with urban and rural development disturb the natural vegetation and have escalated the erosion and sedimentation problem downstream during floods.

Many communities in the watershed, including Santa Cruz, have recorded numerous floods. When the Corps of Engineers began designing a flood control project for Santa Cruz in the 1950's they relied heavily on the data accumulated from the Standard Project Flood (SPF). Then, in December 1955, the flood of record occurred. The discharge in Santa Cruz was estimated to be 39,820 cfs. Seven people died and 28,030 people were displaced from their homes. Damages amounted to about $8.7 million, mostly within Santa Cruz itself. This flood prompted the Corps to reevaluate the design discharge for the project. The new SPF estimate was increased to 50,000 cfs.

Construction of the flood control project began in 1957. It involved constructing levees and excavating 770,000 cubic yards of sediment from the existing channel to increase its slope and capacity. The design channel bottom was lowered as much as six feet below the natural river bottom. In July 1959 the Corps completed the project and deeded the levees to the City of Santa Cruz. The City agreed to maintain the channel to design specifications based on a maintenance and procedure plan supplied by the Corps

Over the next ten years the City intensively developed the "former" floodplain. This development included a new shopping mall located next to the project. In 1975, a survey of the channel centerline indicated that approximately 400,000 cubic yards of sediment had accumulated between the levees, significantly reducing the project's capacity. The City had not dredged the channel annually during this period. Local officials had believed that high winter flows would scour the accumulated sediment and carry it out to sea.

The California Department of Water Resources threatened to dredge the channel for the City and charge it for the cost. The City then began to remove small amounts of the sediment in the channel; as of December 1981 fewer than 100,000 cubic yards had been removed. The City is now unable to finance removal of the remainder of the sediment estimated to cost $3 million initially and $200,000 annual maintenance.

A recent evaluation indicates that at present the levees could contain only a 25 to 30 year flood, or 35,000 cfs without freeboard (Griggs and Paris, 1981). While the FIRM indicates that the 100 year floodplain is contained by the levees, an updated map depicting current conditions would show most of downtown Santa Cruz to lie in the floodplain.

This example illustrates the sorts of problems that can affect a flood control project. The original design discrepancies have contributed to the current situation. Even though the tools and methods available to hydrologists have improved substantially since the 1950's, many hydrologic studies must still be based on scarce streamflow records and other historical data.

OPTIONS FOR ACTION

Policy and Program Elements

If there are levees in your community, adopt a policy and program with the following elements:

1. A policy statement that levees involve risks due to overtopping, inadequate design, inadequate maintenance, internal drainage and other factors;

2. A map of levee location, also indicating safety and degree of provided protection. Inundation zone maps should be prepared for unsafe or inadequate levees;

3. A program for periodic levee inspection. The continued safety of the levee system depends upon maintenance;

4. Protective regulations for areas behind levees. At a minimum, new construction and rebuilding behind levees unable to provide protection from the 100-year flood event should be elevated or floodproofed. For

construction behind levees considered satisfactory to provide protection from a 100-year flood (with necessary freeboard elevations) new construction should be equipped with drainage, pumping and other facilities to prevent internal drainage problems.

5. A regular schedule for communication between engineering, planning and emergency management personnel to provide consideration of levee hazards in land use decisions.

Mapping

Two types of maps can help you reduce risks from levees:

1. Levee location and assessment maps. Maps should be prepared locating all levees in the community and indicating their degree of protection.

2. Inundation map. Flood inundation maps should be prepared for areas behind inadequate or unsafe levees (see sample map, Figure 4-2).

Levee location maps can be prepared from air photos, engineering or public works department records, floodplain maps and field inspections. The levee location and assessment map should show who constructed the levee and who is responsible for its maintenance. Once levees are located, the degree of protection can be assessed with varying degrees of specificity based upon the following types of information:

1. Levee type (see above). This is the minimum indicator of degree of protection.

2. Levee design standard. Expressed as the recurrent interval of the flood that the levee is designed to contain. It can usually be determined from design plans.

3. Comparison of levee height to the 100-year flood elevation. Calculate the number of feet above or feet below or search for previous determinations in engineering reports.

4. Inspection and evaluation of the levee to determine design adequacy and maintenance. This requires field surveys.

If a flood insurance study has been done for your community, it will indicate levees that may provide protection from the 100-year flood (see Appendix 4-A for FEMA requirements). A staff engineer or consultant can make the field inspections necessary to determine intended degree of protection, current conditions and maintenance record for other levees.

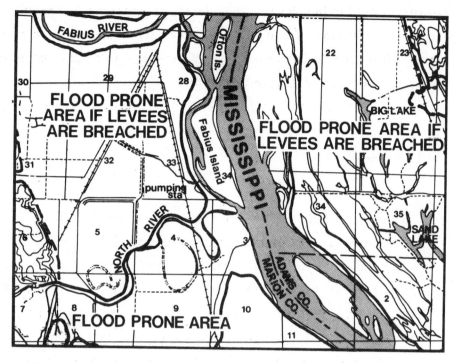

Figure 4-2. Sample map segment showing how levee failure inundation areas could be designated.

Figure 4-3. House behind levee in Soldier's Grove, Wisconsin being elevated after severe flooding in 1978.   Source: T. Hirsch.

Once location and assessment maps are completed, inundation maps can be prepared for areas behind unsafe or inadequate levees. These are prepared much like a normal flood map, making the assumption that the levee will be overtopped. The inundation maps should show:

1. The 100-year floodway and flood fringe as if the levee did not exist.

2. Potential velocity areas at low or weak points in the levee system where overtopping or breaching would most likely occur.

Inundation maps should show areas subject to flooding from internal drainage as well as those at risk due to potential overtopping or breaching. These areas can be identified using historic flood data, local inquiries, topographic maps and field studies. Areas where water is expected to collect to a depth of one foot or more during a specified storm event should be mapped. FEMA's guidelines for mapping of ponding areas, in Appendix 4-A, may be applied.

Regulations

Two types of regulations can reduce flood losses behind levees:

1. Standards for construction, maintenance and rebuilding of levees.

2. Land use controls and building standards for land behind levees.

In formulating your own regulations, check first to see whether your state dam safety or floodplain management program has established minimum standards for construction and maintenance of levees. If so, they may be incorporated by reference in your regulations. Another source of assistance is the U.S. Army Corps of Engineers which has developed standards for the design and construction of levees as well as interior drainage (see references).

In preparing your regulations, a minimum levee crest elevation related to the design flood elevation should be established. At least three feet of elevation (freeboard) should be required over the normal regulatory flood elevation for structures (usually the 100-year flood elevation) to ensure protection from waves, erosion and ice.

Land use standards for buildings and other structures behind "adequate" and "safe" levees raise difficult questions. In one sense, no levee can be considered safe. And yet, to deny the protection afforded by a well-designed and maintained levee may be unreasonable. One approach being considered by Wisconsin is to compare "annual damages" of developing behind a levee, given that the levee will overtop for a flood event which exceeds the design level of the levee. A direct comparison can be made between structures elevated to the 100-year elevation and those built on grade behind a levee. In cases where the natural ground is 5-6 feet lower than the 100-year elevation, annual damages for structures built "on grade" can be greater than structures which are elevated on fill, in spite of "100-year" protection by the levee. To equalize or "optimize" annual damages behind a levee; regulations that require new structures to be elevated on fill must be adopted. Further discussion on this approach is contained in Appendix 4-B.

Non Regulatory Actions
Building Standards

Pennsylvania has developed special building standards for new construction in areas protected by dikes or levees against 100-year flooding. Buildings must be able to resist specified flood forces. A handbook for builders suggests some of the construction practices that meet the requirements (see reference section).

Warning and Evacuation Systems

A warning system and evacuation plan should be established for areas behind unsafe and inadequate levees. Installation of the system could be made a requirement of permits for subdivision or rezoning. All residents and all applicants for construction permits in the floodplain (as mapped without levees) should also be notified that they are in an area protected by such levees and are subject to flooding if the levees are breached or overtopped. Hold an annual public information meeting on the levee warning and evacuation plan.

Inspection and Maintenance

Where a local government agency has constructed or assisted in construction of levees, it should initiate a careful levee inspection and maintenance effort to protect backlying landowners and avoid possible legal liability. Where levees have been constructed by another level of government or by a private entity, communities should conduct their own regular inspection programs as a safety check. They can then require upgrading for inadequate levees. The community engineer or a consultant should make an annual inspection of the levee system. Other community employees should be encouraged to make casual checks for problems whenever they are in the vicinity of levees.

Relocation

Relocation of development should be considered for areas behind inadequate levees or levees where serious and recurring flood damages may result. Soldiers Grove, Wisconsin relocated its entire business district to a hillside location after overtopping of a levee in

1978 caused severe flood damage. Funding came from federal, state and local sources. Some remaining low-lying structures were floodproofed or elevated on fill.

Appendix 4-A: Excerpts from FEMA's Guidelines for Evaluating Local Flood-Control Structures.

The following paragraphs describe procedures for evaluating earthen riverine levees. In evaluating the ability of levee systems to provide protection against the 100-year flood, the following criteria and procedures shall be used.

1. Ownership. Privately owned, operated, or maintained levee systems will not be considered unless a local ordinance or State statute mandates operation and maintenance. Levees for which the community, State, or Federal government has responsibility for operation and maintenance will be considered provided that the criteria discussed below are met.

2. Freeboard. A minimum levee freeboard of 3 feet shall be necessary, with an additional 1 foot of freeboard within 100 feet of either side of structures within the levee or wherever the flow is constricted, such as at bridges. An additional 0.5 foot above this minimu is also required at the upstream end, tapering to the minimum at the downstream end of the levee.

3. Field Inspection and Maintenance. The study contractor must make a field inspection to verify that the levee appears structurally sound and adequately maintained. Certification from a Federal agency, State agency, or a registered professional engineer that the levee meets the minimum freeboard criteria above and that it appears, on visual inspection, to be structurally sound and adequately maintained may be used in lieu of a site specific inspection by the contractor. Levees that have obvious structural defects, or that are obviously lacking in proper maintenance, will not be considered.

4. Internal Drainage. Where credit will be given to levees providing 100-year protection, the adequacy of interior drainage systems will be evaluated. Areas subject to flooding from inadequate interior drainage behind levees will be mapped using standard procedures. Often, shallow flooding zones, or even numbered A zones, may be applicable in these instances.

5. Human Intervention and Operation. In general, levee evaluation shall not consider human intervention (e.g., capping of levees by sandbagging, earthfill, or flashboards) for the purpose of increasing a levee's design level of protection during an imminent flood. Human intervention will only be accepted for the operation of closure structures (e.g., gates or stoplogs) in a levee system designed to provide at least 100-year flood protection, including adequate freeboard as described earlier. Where levee closures are involved, FEMA must review and approve the operation plan prior to the study contractor's assumption that protection against the 100-year flood does exist.

6. Analysis. For the area protected by a levee (inside) providing less than 100-year protection, the base flood elevation shall be computed as if the levee did not exist. For the area outside of such a levee, the elevations to be shown are those obtained from either the flood profile that would exist at the time levee overtopping begins or the profile computed as if the levee did not exist, whichever is higher.

This procedure recognizes the increase in flood elevation in the unprotected area that is caused by the levee itself. This procedure may result in flood elevations being shown as several feet higher on one side of the levee than on the other. Both profiles should be shown in the study report and labeled as "before levee overtopping" and "after levee overtopping", respectively. Separate Floodway Data Tables should be prepared for each side of the levee, and these tables should be adequately labeled. The FIRM work map should show a line, running along the levee centerline, separating the areas of different base flood elevations and zones. ... Floodways will be delineated at the landside toe of mainline and tributary levees that are credited on a map. This will assure that no development will occur on the outside of the levee, which may jeopardize the levee's integrity or effectiveness.

7. Certification. During the course of the Flood Insurance Study, when the study contractor determines that an area of a community has no special flood hazards because it is protected by a flood-control structure, the contractor must obtain from the agency responsible for the structure a written statement that the structure is properly designed, constructed, maintained, and operated to provide protection from the 100-year flood. This certification must be accompanied by copies of the applicable operation and maintenance plans and forwarded to FEMA for approval as soon as possible.

8. Exception Procedures. FEMA will accept certification from another Federal agency that an existing levee system is designed, constructed, maintained and operated to provide protection against the 100-year flood in lieu of the specific requirements of items 2, 3, and 5 above. Under certain circumstances, FIA may also grant exceptions to the above requirements or approve alternate analysis techniques. The Study Contractor must obtain written approval of all such exceptions or alternate analyses from the PO before proceeding.

Appendix 4-B: Excerpts from the Levee Policy Proposed by the Wisconsin Department of Natural Resources, 1984.

(1) **GENERAL.** Adequately designed, constructed and maintained levees, floodwalls and channel impvovements provide for reduced damages and relief from flooding. The following standards shall apply to municipal floodplain zoning regulations for areas landward of levees, floodwalls and channel improvements.

(2) **ADEQUATE LEVEES OR FLOODWALLS.**

(a) A levee or floodwall shall be considered adequate if all of the following criteria and the requirements of sub. (b) are met:

1.   a. Except as provided in sub. par. b. the minimum top elevation of the levee or floodwall shall be 3 feet above the calculated 500 year flood profile with the flood confined riverward of the proposed levee or floodwall, under either of the following conditions in this subparagraph.

    b. The minimum top elevation of a levee may be adjusted by the department to an elevation of not less than 3 feet above the calculated 100 year profile. with the flood confined riverward of the proposed levee or floodwall, under either of the following conditions in this subparagraph.

        i.   If the calculated expected annual damages to structures landward of the proposed levee or floodwall that do not comply with [floodplain regulations] are equal to or less than the calculated expected annual damages to structures landward of the proposed levee or floodwall that do comply with [floodplain regulations] at a flood with a recurrence interval of less than 500 years, the minimum top elevation of the levee or floodwall shall be at least 3 feet above the calculated profile for that flood.

        ii.   If the department is satisfied that the additional 3 feet of height above the calculated profile is not necessary to prevent flood damages due to overtopping of the levee during the design recurrence interval flood, it may waive the requirement for a portion of this added height.

2.   U.S. Army Corps of Engineers standards for design and construction of levees and floodwalls shall be the minimum standard for levees and floodwalls.

3.   Interior drainage shall be provided using designated ponding areas, pumps or other similar means, in accordance with U.S. Army Corps of Engineers standards.

4.   An emergency action plan, concurred in by the division of emergency government and approved by the department, shall be in effect for the area behind the levee or floodwall that would be in the floodplain without the proposed levee or floodwall in place.

5. The municipality shall provide notification to all persons receiving construction permits in the area behind the proposed levee or floodwall that would be in the floodplain without the proposed levee or floodwall in place that they are in an area protected by a levee or floodwall which is subject to flooding if the levee or floodwall is overtopped.

6. The levee or floodwall shall be annually inspected and certified, by a professional engineer registered in Wisconsin, that the levee or floodwall meets the standards in Subds. 1. to 5. Annual reports of the inspection and certification shall be sent to the department for review.

7. The department reviews and approves the material submitted under subds. 1. to 5.

(b) No obstruction to flood flows caused by construction of levees or floodwalls may be allowed unless amendments are made to the floodway lines, regional flood profiles, floodplain zoning maps and floodplain zoning ordinances. Calculations of the effect of the levee or floodwall on regional flood heights shall compare existing conditions with the condition of the regional flood confined riverward of the proposed levee or floodwall.

(c) Floodplain areas protected by an adequate levee or floodwall shall be designated as flood fringe but may be regulated as areas outside of the floodplain unless the department determines that the levee or floodwall is no longer adequate.

(3) **INADEQUATE LEVEES OR FLOODWALLS.** If the department determines that an existing levee or floodwall does not meet the criteria of sub. (2)(a), all floodplain areas landward of the inadequate levee or floodwall shall be regulated as if the levee or floodwall does not exist.

(5) **NEW CONSTRUCTION OF LEVEES, FLOODWALLS OR CHANNEL IMPROVEMENTS.** No anticipated changes in the flood protection elevations or floodplain and floodway limits, based upon proposed levees, floodwalls or channel improvements, may be effective until the improvements are constructed, operative and approved by the department.

SELECTED REFERENCES ON FLOODING IN AREAS BELOW INADEQUATE LEVEES

Emergency Preparedness News, 1984, (March 7). Silver Spring, Maryland: Emergency Preparedness News.

Federal Emergency Management Agency, et al., 1982, *Interagency Hazard Mitigation Report--Allen County, Indiana*. Washington, D.C.: FEMA.

Griggs, G. B. and L. Paris, 1982, *Flood Control Failure: San Lorenz River, California*. Environmental Management 6(5):407-417.

National Research Council, 1982, *A Levee Policy for the National Flood Insurance Program*. Washington, D.C.: National Academy Press.

Pennsyslvania Department of Community Affairs, 1981, *Handbook of Flood Resistant Construction Specifications, Suggested for Use in Areas Protected by Dikes and Levees*. Harrisburg, Pennsylvlania: Dept. of Community Affairs.

Platt, Rutherford H., 1982, *The Jackson Flood of 1979--A Public Policy Disaster*. American Planning Association Journal (Spring): 219-231.

Vogt, R. and R. Watson, 1983, *How Dams and Levees Affect Flood Hazard Areas: Evaluating the Standards*. Prepared by the Wisconsin Dept. of Natural Resources for the Federal Emergency Management Agency. Washington, D.C.: FEMA.

Watson, R.M., 1984, *Expected Annual Damages: with and without levees*. Wisconsin Dept. of Natural Resources. Unpublished.

CHAPTER 5: AREAS BELOW UNSAFE DAMS

THE HAZARD

While severe loss of life and property from catastrophic failures of dams such as the Grand Teton Dam have focused national attention on the safety of large dams, the aggregate losses from the failure of many smaller dams during major flood events may be even greater. Dam failure -- the wall of water rushing downstream, the devastation of property, the loss of life -- is a threat to thousands of communities.

Dams have been a part of civilization for several millennia. Archaeological studies of ancient China, India, Iran and Egypt display evidence of dams 6,000 years ago. Over the centuries, significant advances have been made in both construction techniques and the size of the structure. Still, impoundment of water is never without risk. Millions of people live and work in the shadow of dams. No matter how safely dams are designed, constructed and maintained, the threat of failure due to structural failure, earthquakes or sabotage exists.

When a dam fails, the unexpectedness and high velocity of the water make the damage severe. Once signs of dam failure become visible, breaching often occurs within hours. There is little time for evacuation.

Over time, dams magnify the downstream risk of flooding with or without failure. Dams often attract new floodplain development with the availability of water, power or recreation opportunities. Dams create a sense of flood protection which is, in part, false. Reservoir sedimentation can significantly reduce flood control capability. Competing uses of the reservoir can impair flood control since those relying on the dam for recreation and water supply (including irrigators, manufacturers and residential users) often press for continued high pool levels. When floods occur, little or no reservoir storage space may remain.

EXISTING MITIGATION EFFORTS

Federal Efforts

Two dam failures in the early 1970s encouraged Congress to adopt national dam safety legislation. One hundred twenty-five people died in the failure of a dam created by a mine refuse embankment on Buffalo Creek in West Virginia. Less than four months later, 238 persons lost their lives when the Canyon Lake Dam failed near Rapid City, South Dakota.

In adopting the National Dam Inspection Act of 1972 (P.L. 92-367) Congress required the U.S. Army Corps of Engineers to inspect all dams in the United States except those under the jurisdiction of certain federal agencies and various other classes of dams. The Corps was also required to compile an inventory of all dams in the nation. Congress provided funding for the inspection of all high hazard dams after yet another disaster: the November 6, 1977 failure of the Kelley Barnes Lake Dam at Toccoa, Georgia.

Under the 1972 law, the U.S. Army Corps of Engineers classified all dams (totalling 67,451) in the United States over 25 feet in height or impounding 50 or more acre-feet of water. Dams were classified as "high", "significant" or "low" hazard depending on the degree of anticipated damage if the dam failed:

High Hazard - A failure of a high hazard dam would result in loss of life and extreme flood damage.

Significant Hazard - A dam is considered a significant hazard if extreme flood damage would occur upon failure.

Low Hazard - A low hazard dam would cause little or moderate damage upon failure.

Between December, 1977 and October, 1981, the Corps of Engineers inspected over 8800 high hazard dams. About one-third were judged unsafe. A dam was classified as unsafe if it had a deficiency that, if left uncorrected, could result in a failure with consequent loss of life and substantial property damage. Many unsafe dams were so classified because their spillways could not pass the maximum probable flood.

After the failure of the Grand Teton Dam in Idaho on April 23, 1977 (see Figure 5-1), President Carter directed federal agencies to convene an ad hoc interagency committee to coordinate dam safety programs. In 1979, federal agencies concerned about dam safety published national guidelines for planning, design, construction, operation and regulation of dams (see references).

Efforts to reduce risks from unsafe or inadequate dams have also been adopted at the state level. Most states have dam safety programs that establish minimum design standards. Far fewer have maintenance specifications or a mandated dam inspection program. Some states require periodic reports by dam owners and authorize inspections. See Appendix 5-A for an example.

Figure 5-1. The Teton Dam, a Bureau of Reclamation project, collapsed in 1976 killing 11 people and causing millions of dollars in damages. The dam's collapse illustrated, once again, that structural solutions to flood problems are not without inherent risks.

Safety surveys for both new and existing dams have been carried out by many states. Some states, such as California and Iowa, map inundation zones below all new dams. Colorado requires the owners of unsafe dams to prepare inundation zone maps. A suggested inundation zone mapping procedure from Colorado is included in Appendix 5-B. Wisconsin has drafted guidelines requiring community regulation of areas below unsafe dams (see Appendix 5-C).

OPTIONS FOR ACTION

Policy and Program Elements

A community with dams or downstream of dams in other governmental jurisdictions should adopt a policy and program with the following elements:

1. A policy statement recognizing the inherent dangers in all dams due to unexpected failure or overtopping by a flood exceeding the level for which the dam was designed, by sedimentation, by earthquake or by other causes. It may be prudent to assume that any dam can fail.

2. An assessment of all dams within or affecting the community to determine the degree of protection provided, maintenance or rehabilitation needs for each dam, and of the need for land use controls or emergency preparedness below the dam.

3. A process for regular review and updating of this information.

4. Maps of the inundation zones for areas below all unsafe or inadequate dams.

5. A set of stringent floodplain regulations for inundation areas below unsafe or inadequate dams.

6. Dam safety regulations requiring owners of unsafe or inadequate dams to repair or upgrade such structures.

7. A flood warning system and evacuation plan for areas below unsafe dams.

8. A schedule of regular (at least yearly) meetings with dam owners to insure proper dam operation and maintenance and to inform owners of new or proposed downstream developments. Reiterate your mutual interests in protecting lives and property and in avoiding liability for any damages.

9.   A schedule of regular communication between engineering, planning and emergency management personnel to consider dam safety in land use decisions and to update preparedness systems to reflect new developments.

10. A policy to give floodwater storage high priority in setting levels and timing drawdown of reservoirs. Water users and the public should be educated about the need for flood storage.

Mapping

Two types of maps or surveys are needed to reduce threats posed by unsafe or inadequate dams:

1.   An inventory of all dams in the community with an evaluation of their safety and effectiveness, and,

2.   Inundation zone mapping for dams considered unsafe or inadequate.

A preliminary survey of dams in your community may be based, in part, on state and federal surveys. Be aware that state and federal surveys often do not include small structures which may be of local concern. Air photos and field surveys can also be used to locate structures. Local conservation officers are also often familiar with the location and condition of dams. Once dams have been located, a more detailed investigation of safety parameters is needed. State and federal surveys may help here as well. A number of sources of technical assistance are available to assist in evaluating dams. If data are not available, it will be necessary to have surveys done by an engineer or engineering geologist.

In evaluating dams, consider design, construction and maintenance. Check spillway capacity even if the dam appears safe in other respects. A 1971 study by Biswas and Chatterjee of 300 dam failures concluded that 35% of them were the direct result of floods in excess of the spillway capacity. Foundation problems such as seepage, piping, excess pore pressures, inadequate cutoffs, fault movement and settlement of rockslides were the cause of 25% of the failures. Improper design or construction, inferior materials, wave action, acts of war or lack of proper operation and/or maintenance accounted for the remaining 40% of the failures (see Figure 5-2).

Once the location and degree of protection afforded by existing dams have been determined, inundation zones should be mapped for unsafe or inadequate dams. The inundation zone is the area that would be flooded in the event of a failure. While a dam may fail on a sunny day, the most likely and most dangerous situation is failure during a flood when water levels are highest (see Figure 5-3). It is advisable, therefore, to identify the area that would be inundated by failure during the 100-year flood. Both the broad inundation zone and the floodway within this zone should be outlined.

There are several published methods for mapping inundation zones (see Appendix 5-B for one example.) The analysis should be done by a professional engineer. Technical assistance may be available from your state dam safety program or the U.S. Army Corps of Engineers.

The inundation zone map has four important uses:

1. To establish the regulatory jurisdiction for zoning;
2. To identify the area needing evacuation or other emergency procedures in the event of failure of the dam;
3. To promote consideration of the risk in land use planning;
4. To build citizen awareness of the potential hazard.

Regulations

Dam safety regulations should address three topics:

1. Dam design standards;
2. Dam safety inspection and maintenance requirements; and
3. Zoning of downstream areas.

State dam safety programs may already address the first two.

<u>Design standards</u>

Design standards are most commonly adopted at the state level, but counties and cities in some states have adopted their own standards. Design standards should apply to new dams and to the reconstruction of existing dams. Since dam specifications vary with the purpose of the dam, location and other factors, each design should be reviewed by a staff engineer or consultant. The reviewer must judge whether the proposed design presents a hazard to the health, safety or welfare of the public.

Some state dam safety laws establish specific spillway requirements based on existing development and existing land use controls in the vicinity of the dam site. Adequate spillway capacity can prevent overtopping and upstream flooding from floods up to and including the design capacity of the structure. To ensure that the construction is done according to plan, a professional engineer can be required to supervise the operation. The owner can be required to file a bond.

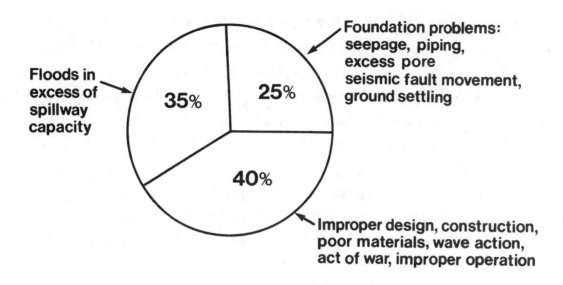

Floods in excess of spillway capacity → 35%

25% ← **Foundation problems: seepage, piping, excess pore seismic fault movement, ground settling**

40%

← **Improper design, construction, poor materials, wave action, act of war, improper operation**

Figure 5-2. Causes of dam failure.

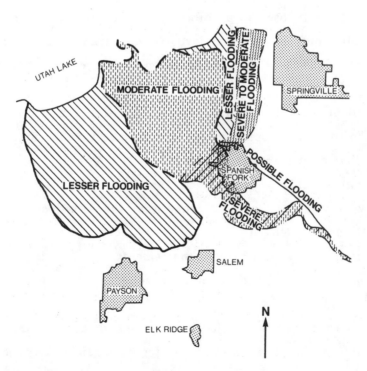

Figure 5-3. The worse-case inundation scenario from the failure of the Thistle Dam. A simply drawn map can help inform residents who are at risk and ensure that the risk of dam failure is considered in land use decisions. Source: National Research Council.

Inspection and Maintenance

Inspection and maintenance should be required by your dam safety ordinance. If your state has a dam safety law, find out whether it applies to the dams in your community. If so, obtain the results or schedule of inspections. Dams are also inspected by the Federal Energy Regulatory Commission and under the Federal Dam Safety Inspection Program. These reports will be useful.

Whether or not the dams in your community fall under one of these programs, establish a schedule for regular (at least yearly) inspection by municipal staff or consultants. Encourage casual checks by municipal employees whose work brings them into the vicinity. If problems arise, request inspection by state or federal officials. Appendix 5-C contains a quick inspection procedure.

In your contacts with dam owners, review their maintenance plans. Obtain written certification of their ability and intent to operate and maintain the dam.

An unsafe dam may legally be a nuisance. If a dam owner cannot or will not restore safe conditions, contact state dam safety officials or your community's legal counsel.

Zoning

The best way to avoid danger in the event of a dam failure is to prohibit or carefully control development in inundation zones. Floodplain zoning, subdivision and building code requirements can be used to prohibit new development in the high risk area below dams or to establish performance standards for elevation of new structures. The most critical area is in the floodway of the inundation zone where water velocities will be very high.

Areas below dams should be zoned based on the design and structural integrity of individual dams. The following approach has been proposed by the State of Wisconsin:

Below dams that meet safety requirements:

Developed areas should be zoned as if the dam is in place during the 100-year flood. Undeveloped areas should be zoned as if the dam does not exist since it may become unsafe or be removed.

Below dams that do not meet safety requirements:

Developed and undeveloped areas should be zoned as if the dam would fail during the 100-year flood.

Such zoning changes can be carried out by amendment to existing zoning, floodplain management, subdivision, building, stormwater management or other regulation.

Figure 5-4. Buffalo Creek, West Virginia: Aftermath of a dam failure. The tangled wreckage shows the force unleashed when a dam fails. One hundred, twenty-five people lost their lives in this dam failure.   Source: unknown.

Figure 5-5. Routine dam inspection is a necessary part of a dam safety program. This rather dramatic erosion problem was identified during a routine inspection.   Source: Minnesota Dept. of Natural Resources.

Nonregulatory Actions

<u>Warning and Evacuation Systems</u>

Any dam with development in the inundation zone of the maximum probable flood should have a warning and evacuation system. Dam owners can be required to install and operate the system. Emergency plans should be discussed at a public information meeting after notification of all residents in the inundation zone.

<u>Reservoir Management</u>

Reservoir management for flood control means regulating water levels and flows from the pool behind the dam to allow for storage of flood waters. Management procedures for flood control should be built into dam operating procedures and into legally established levels and flows. Large reservoirs that are used for irrigation or power generation require particularly careful computation of drawdown curves based on long-term precipitation records and hydrologic models in order to maximize water storage or power production while allowing for flood storage.

For smaller reservoirs where storage capacity can be more quickly created, operating plans for accommodating floodwaters are often more easily prepared. Pool levels can either be dropped for a specified length of time to accommodate anticipated seasonal flooding or the discharge can be increased in response to current weather forecasts.

Appendix 5-A: A Sample Dam Safety Inspection Guide.

insert credits here

CONDITION OF DAM

I. EMBANKMENTS

a. *Seepage*: indicate the location of seepage areas and estimate quantity of flow. Note whether flow is clear or carries material.

b. *Slope stability*: note areas of slumps or slides. Look for soft ground, depressions, or wet areas on the embankment. Note evidence of recent movement or trees which are not growing vertically.

c. *Surface erosion*: note bare patches of soil or other evidence of erosion.

d. *Animal burrows*: inspect all earthen embankments for evidence of burrowing animals.

e. *Embankment-structure junctions*: examine these junctions for evidence of sliding, deformation or movement. Look for potential slippage planes and weakness zones. Carefully check for seepage and erosion along junction planes.

f. *Slope protection*: note presence and condition of riprap along toe of embankments.

g. *Vegetation*: the embankment should have a good covering of grass, free from broad leaf vegatation, shrubs and trees. Note areas that lack suitable cover and especially note the presence of large trees on the dikes.

II. SPILLWAY(S)

a. *Surface condition*: Check for spillway spalling and areas of broken or missing concrete. Check for effects of cavitation and freeze/thaw.

b. *Cracks*: Note width of existing cracks. Noting crack widths will allow monitoring of structural integrity.

c. *Joints*: look for misalignments or evidence that joint size has changed.

III. GATES

a. *Steel, timber*: note number and size of each gate section.

b. *Gate seals*: examine for leakage and seal deterioration.

c. *Gate pins*: look for cracking of concrete near pins which could indicate potential failure. Check for pin deterioration, including metal corrosion.

d. *Gate hoist and chains*: determine if gate is operable and the condition of the lifting equipment.

IV. MISCELLANEOUS

a.   *Debris*: examine trash racks for accumulated debris. Examine interior of drop inlets and outlet pipes for lodged trash and debris which could reduce flood capacity. Note elevation of debris line around flowage to indicate level fluctuations and operation of the dam.

b.   *Walkway and railing*: examine for missing or broken railings, broken steps, or other safety related hazards. Check for access to controls during high-water.

c.   *Paint*: look for rust spots or other evidence of deteriorated paint (particularly on structural members of the dam).

d.   *Downstream apron*: check for spalling, slumping, uplift, cracking or other deterioration. Note any undercutting of apron and give dimensions.

e.   *Stilling basin*: examine stilling basin for scour and undercutting at the toe of the dam. Check for displaced or deteriorated stone. Check depth of water in the stilling basin if possible.

f.   *Foundation seepage*: check for evidence of seepage, aquatic vegetation or areas of discoloration. Note any changes from past seepage patterns, particularly new areas of seepage. Estimate quantity of seepage flow if possible.

g.   *Downstream channel*: check for erosion and scour which could undermine the dam. Also look for buildups of material (shoals or islands) which might indicate turbulent flows.

h.   *Other observations*: list all other observations which bear on the safety and performance of the dam. Include past evidence of overtopping or failures. Include any cultural changes, such as subdivision development below the dam, which could change the hazard classification of the dam.

BOATING SAFETY

a.   *Warning devices and signs*: describe the location of all signs and devices. Indicate need for new signs and adequacy of existing signs.

b.   *Portage signs and facilities*: indicate what provisions are needed for portaging and if such provisions have been made and are adequate.

HYDROPOWER USER

a.   *Last date used for power*: indicate, if known.

b.   *Current installed capacity*: list rated kilowatt on generating unit.

c.   *Average power output during inspection*: list power output while you were inspecting the dam (also any flow not being used for power).

Appendix 5-B. Excerpts from "A Method for the Rapid Approximation of Dam Failure Floodplains in Colorado."

by William P. Stanton, P.E., Supervising Water Resource Specialist, Flood Control and Floodplain Management Section, Colorado Water Conservation Board, July, 1983.

Preface.

Since 1890, there have been at least 130 known dam failures in Colorado. Following the failure of Lawn Lake dam and subsequent flooding through the town of Estes Park, Colorado on July 15, 1982, considerable attention has been focused on reducing damages from potential dam failure floods.

In January 1983, state agencies prepared a Flood Hazard Mitigation Plan for Colorado which included recommendations to improve state programs in dam safety, floodplain management and emergency preparedness. One of the ideas was a recommendation that the Colorado Water Conservation Board (CWCB) develop a technique for mapping approximate dam failure floodplains below all dams in Colorado. Because no state agency had a program to map dam failure inundation zones, the idea was to develop a manual which would outline a simple, cost effective procedure which would allow dam owners and local officials to determine an approximate inundation zone themselves.

On June 1, 1983, Governor Lamm signed House Bill 1416 which, among other things, directed the Division of Water Resources (State Engineer) to prepare a report on approximately 238 dams in the state formerly classified as "high hazard." The hazard rating is determined by the potential for loss of human life or property damage in the area downstream for a dam and does not pertain to the safety of the structure.

Each report included a map indicating the possible extent of flooding in the event of failure to a point where such floodwaters would no longer exceed the boundaries of the 100-year floodplain. The dam failure floodplain for approximately 337 "moderate hazard", 1,680 "low hazard" dams and thousands of highway embankments and stock ponds which were not included in H.B. 1416 remain to be mapped.

Knowing where the water might go from a dam failure flood may help to reduce development in areas which effect the hazard rating of the dam. It may also help local officials plan for emergency response activities which could reduce flood damages and save lives.

1.0 Purpose.

The purpose of this document is to provide dam owners, floodplain managers, emergency planners and citizens with a quick and simple method to find out where the water from a dam failure might be reasonably expected to go. The suggested level of detail is intended to be consistent with readily available base map information. The approximate flood boundaries developed with this method are for planning purposes only and should be conservative, that is, the flooded area should be slightly overestimated.

2.0 Tools You Will Need.

A. Best available topographic base map(s) for the stream below the dam. The 7.5 minute, 1:24,000 scale quadrangle maps published for sale by the U.S. Geological Survey ...are recommended....

B. Engineer's scale (but you don't have to be an engineer).

C. Colored pencils and a heavy black felt tip pen.

D. Information about the dam including location and height or drainage area.

3.0 Dam Failure Floodplain Boundary

Procedure to Delineate Approximate   Dam Failure Floodplain Boundaries

1. Starting at the top of the dam and working downstream to the end of the study reach, draw a reference line down the center of the channel and mark each mile post.. Making this center line and marking regular intervals is called "stationing."

2. Find where the topographic map contours cross the river and mark each point on the reference line. 3. Find the height of the dam in feet measured from the top of the spillway to the lowest point in the channel just below the dam.

4. From the height of the dam, estimate the depth of the dam failure floodplain at intervals below the dam based on the assumed rate of attenuation given below.

Miles downstream from dam	Assumed flood depth as a percent of dam height
0 - 1	100
1 - 2	70
2 - 10	60
10 - 20	50
20 - 30	40
30 - 40	30
40 - 80	20
80+	10

5. Using the contour interval on the topographic base map, ... compute the horizontal scaling ratios for each stream interval to be applied in the downstream direction from where the topographic map contours cross the river.

6. Locate the flood contours on the channel and extend them perpendicular to the direction of flow until they meet the corresponding ground contour.

7. Connect the endpoints of the flood contours, looking out for islands and an even spacing of flood contours. Flood boundaries should cross ground contours on a tangent.

8.   At major obstructions, such as highway or railroad bridges, an adjustment in the flood depths may be appropriate to reflect water backed up just upstream of the obstruction and shallower depth just downstream of the obstruction. By advancing or bending flood contours slightly downstream, a greater depth will be apparent, and vice versa.

The procedure to estimate flood boundaries may be conservative for the following reasons:

1.   The topographic map contours show top of the water and not the true thalweg (lowest point in the channel). The depth of flow that was in the river at the time of mapping will be added to the assumed depth.

2.   A conservative stair-step approximation of the assumed attenuation curve was used to interpret flood depths.

3.   The flood boundary is shown as a heavy line which, on a scale of 1 inch equals 2,000 feet, may be as much as 200 feet wide.

Appendix 5-C: Wisconsin's Proposed Guidelines for Community Regulation of Areas Below Dams.

(1)   **General.** Adequately designed, constructed and maintained dams provide reduced damages and relief from flooding for developed areas. Areas downstream of dams shall be zoned and regulated by municipalities with floodplain zoning ordinances in compliance with the standards in this section, to reduce potential loss of life and property located downstream of the dams. Except as provided in sub. (2), areas downstream of all dams shall be delineated on floodplain maps.

(2)   **Exemptions.** All dams having a structural height of 6 feet or less, or a storage capacity of 15 acre feet or less, and all dams having a structural height of more than 6 feet but less than 25 feet with a storage capacity of 50 acre feet or less are exempt from the requirements of this section.

(3)   **Safe dams.**

    (a) A dam is considered safe if the requirements in this paragraph are met.

    1.   The dam is structurally adequate to meet the conditions in ss. NR 333.05(2)(g) and 333.07(4)(b).

    2.   The dam is hydraulically adequate to meet the standards in s. NR 333.07(2).

    3.   The dam has been certified by a professional engineer, registered in Wisconsin, to meet the requirements of subds. 1. and 2.;

    4.   Written assurance of the dam owner's ability to operate and maintain the dam in good condition is obtained from the dam owner:

    5.   An emergency action plan to minimize loss of human life has been adopted by the municipality for the area downstream of the dam based on the assumption that the dam fails during the regional flood; and

    6.   The department reviews and approves the material submitted under subds. 1. to 5.

    (b) Developed areas downstream of a safe dam shall be zoned and regulated assuming that the dam is in place during the regional flood.

    (c) Undeveloped areas downstream of a safe dam shall be zoned and regulated assuming that the dam does not exist.

(4)   **Unsafe dams.**

    (a) if an existing dam does not meet the standards in Sub. (3)(a), the dam is considered unsafe.

    (b) Both developed and undeveloped areas downstream of an unsafe dam shall be zoned and regulated assuming that dam failure occurs during the regional flood.

(c) The regional flood profile of the area downstream of the dam shall be calculated in accordance with s. NR 333.05(2)(b)

(5) **Construction of new dams.**

(a) Dams constructed after the effective date of this rule shall be considered safe if the requirements in sub. (3)(a) are met.

(b) Developed areas downstream of the construction of a new dam shall be zoned and regulated as if the dam does not exist until construction is 100% complete and all the conditions of sub. (3)(a) are met.

SELECTED REFERENCES ON FLOODING BELOW INADEQUATE DAMS

Ad Hoc Interagency Committee on Dam Safety, 1979, *Federal Guidelines for Dam Safety*. Washington, D.C.: Federal Coordinating Council for Science, Engineering and Technology, Washington, D.C. (Reprinted by the Federal Emergency Management Agency.)

Dewberry and Davis, 1982, *Dam Safety Mapping Pilot Study*. Prepared for the Federal Emergency Management Agency. Washington, D.C.: FEMA.

Federal Emergency Management Agency, 1982, *Dam Safety Research--Current, Planned and Future*. Washington, D.C.: FEMA.

Graham, W.J. and C.A. Brown, 1982, *The Lawn Lake Dam Failure*. Washington, D.C.: Bureau of Reclamation, U.S. Dept. of the Interior.

Jansen, R.B., 1980, *Dams and Public Safety*. Water Resource Technical Report. Washington, D.C.: U.S. Dept. of the Interior.

National Academy of Sciences, 1982, Committee on Safety of Non-federal Dams. *Safety of Non-federal Dams--A review of the Federal Role*. Washington, D.C.: National Academy Press. (Reprinted by the Federal Emergency Management Agency.)

National Academy of Sciences, 1983, Committee on the Safety of Existing Dams. *Safety of Existing Dams--Evaluation and Improvement*. Washington D.C. National Academy Press.

National Weather Service, 1981, DAMBRK - The NWS Dam Break Flood Forecasting Model *Users Manual*. Hydrologic Research Laboratory, National Weather Service, National Oceanic and Atmospheric Administration. Washington, D.C.: NOAA.

Owen, H. J., 1980, *Flood Emergency Plans--Guidelines for Corps Dams*. Prepared for the Hydrologic Engineering Center. Davis, California: U.S. Army Corps of Engineers.

Tschantz, B. A., 1983, *Report on Review of State Non-federal Dam Safety Programs*. Prepared by the Civil Engineering Department, University of Tennessee. Washington, D.C.: Federal Emergency Management Agency.

Vogt, R. and R. Watson, 1983, *How Dams and Levees Affect Flood Hazard Areas: Evaluating the Standards*. Prepared by the Wisconsin Dept. of Natural Resources. Washington, D.C.: Federal Emergency Management Agency.

CHAPTER 6: COASTAL FLOODING AND EROSION

THE HAZARD

From California to the Great Lakes to Cape Cod, houses built along the immediate coastline are often destroyed by a combination of caving of bluffs or erosion of beaches and dunes and flooding. Combined erosion and flooding affects all coasts but is particularly serious on barrier islands and on exposed Atlantic and Gulf Coasts and the Great Lakes. In 1971, the U.S. Army Corps of Engineers estimated that a quarter of the national shore front (20,500 miles) was subject to significant erosion. While erosion losses were not systematically tallied, average annual losses due to erosion in 1975 were conservatively estimated to exceed $300 million.

Erosion increases flood damages in several ways. Once a beach or dune is eroded, high velocity waves penetrate further inland, often destroying buildings and infrastructure. In addition, erosion can permanently lower the elevation of beaches, bluffs and dunes, resulting in deeper flooding. Erosion also undermines pilings and foundations, causing structures to topple into the water. Erosion and flood damage may be indistinguishable during major storms.

Coastal erosion is caused by hurricanes, winter storms, rising sea levels, tides and currents, and human activities. Most erosion damage occurs in major storms since the erosive force of water is related to its velocity.

Coastal erosion and flooding affect bluff, beach, dune and marsh areas somewhat differently:

Bluff erosion occurs along the California and Oregon coasts; Lakes Michigan, Superior and Erie; the Chesapeake Bay and unconsolidated shoreland areas along the Gulf and Atlantic coasts such as Cape Cod, Massachusetts. Bluff erosion is most serious where the coast consists of unconsolidated sediments and is caused primarily by waves. (See Figure 6-1). Other causes include currents, sea level rise, surface runoff and the activities of man.

Bluff erosion is irreversible. Unless the bluff is stabilized or the building moved back, houses built along bluffs are sooner or later destroyed. Many houses built at what was once considered a safe distance from the edge are now threatened. Bluff stabilization or relocation of homes are both extremely expensive.

The enormous erosive force of storm waves is illustrated by the following description from a report on Great Lakes erosion: Very few people, who have not lived on the shore, can visualize the extraordinary energies that can be thrown against the shore by breaking waves. At Duluth, waves 23 feet high have been recorded with hydraulic pressures of 2370 pounds per square foot. In November 1950, storm waves on Lake Michigan moved a concrete cap on a breakwater at Gary, Indiana. The concrete cap, 200 feet long and weighing 2,600 tons, was moved four feet by waves 13.5 feet high. The wave pressure required to move the cap was calculated to have been as much as 2,500 pounds per square foot (Hanson, et al., 1976).

Beach erosion occurs along all of the coasts but is most serious along the eastern seaboard. Rapid erosion of wetlands rather than beaches along the Louisiana coast threatens much of the Mississippi Delta. Wetlands rather than beaches form the interface here between the land and open sea. Most beaches are eroded by currents, waves and high tides each year and, to some extent are rebuilt by the same natural processes. Beaches often retreat and rebuild dozens or even hundreds of feet each year.

Were it not for sea level rise, discussed below, most beaches would naturally rebuild. Although beaches naturally rebuild, houses constructed on eroding beaches do not. Combined flooding and erosion is a serious problem not only for buildings located on beaches but those in backlying areas subject to wave runup. During major storms, waves can run up beaches to elevations twice the storm wave height above normal sea level.

Dune erosion is a serious problem along the Gulf and Atlantic coasts but also occurs along Lake Michigan and some stretches of the California, Oregon and Washington shorelands. Dunes are located shoreward of beaches and may rise from three to more than 100 feet in height. Geologically, they are part of the beach system and provide a reservoir of sand for the beach. Historically, dunes are eroded and rebuilt by wind and waves, gradually moving inland with sea level rise.

Severe erosion of dunes is common during a major hurricane or during a winter storm like the Ash Wednesday Northeaster of 1962. The '62 storm leveled the dune system along much of the New York, New Jersey, Maryland and Virginia coasts, destroying thousands of houses built on, in front of and immediately behind the dunes. People continue to locate houses on dunes to take advantage of the view and because their height above the water gives a sense, albeit false, of safety from flooding.

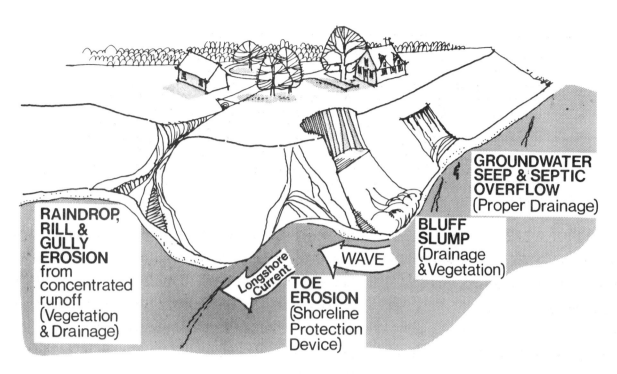

RAINDROP, RILL & GULLY EROSION from concentrated runoff (Vegetation & Drainage)

Longshore Current

TOE EROSION (Shoreline Protection Device)

WAVE

BLUFF SLUMP (Drainage & Vegetation)

GROUNDWATER SEEP & SEPTIC OVERFLOW (Proper Drainage)

Figure 6-1. Bluff erosion problems and some solutions.
Source: Great Lakes Basin Commission.

Figure 6-2. Shore erosion control structure in Massachusetts.
Source: Jon Kusler.

Permanent recession of beaches and dunes along the Pacific, is primarily due to sea level rise. Until recently, the sea was rising at the rate of about 1 foot per century. Now, this rate may be much greater, resulting in thousands of feet of shoreline retreat. (See insert).

Importance of Sea Level Rise

The U.S. Environmental Protection Agency (EPA) has projected serious increases in sea level as a result of melting of the polar ice caps due to concentration of atmospheric CO_2 and other greenhouse gases (Hoffman, et al., 1983). EPA concluded that a global rise of between 4.8 feet and 7.0 feet by year 2100 is possible. A one foot per century rise in sea levels will, on the average, cause beaches to migrate inland 100 to 300 foot per century. The report describes the effect of sea level rise:

"Sea level rise will have three major types of physical effects: shoreline retreat, increased flooding, and landward movement of salt water. Shorelines will retreat because very low land will be inundated and other land along the shore will erode. For example, a thirty centimeter (one foot) rise in sea level would erode most sandy beaches along the Atlantic and Gulf coasts at least thirty meters (one hundred feet)."

"Whether or not EPA's projections, assumptions, and methods are fully accepted, there is ample documentation of serious long-term increases in sea level and landward migration of beaches, dunes, bluffs and barrier islands along ocean and Great Lakes shores. For further reading on sea level rise see the paper by Hoffman, et al. in the bibliography."

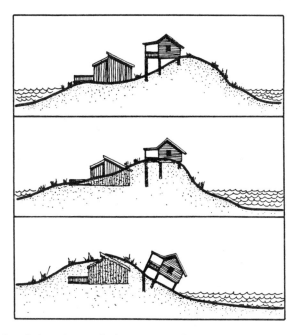

Figure 6-3. Barrier islands and dunes are forever shifting.
Source: Jon Kusler.

Figure 6-4. Beach erosion threatens tens of thousands of structures on
barrier islands along the Atlantic coast.   Source: NOAA.

Figure 6-5. This bluff along Lake Michigan near Racine, Wisconsin is pictured on a calm day to highlight its vulnerability to wave action. Storm waves on Lake Michigan have been calculated to wield forces of up to 2500 pounds per square foot. Source: Jon Kusler.

Figure 6-6: Buildings in the path of coastal floods seldom just get wet. Erosion worsens flooding as well as causing physical damage. Source: Jon Kusler.

EXISTING MITIGATION EFFORTS

Efforts have been made at all levels of government to separately address coastal flooding and erosion. While damages have been reduced, the combined erosion and flooding problem requires a coordinated approach to further reduce losses.

Federal

Four major federal programs address coastal erosion. These include:

Federal Erosion Control

In 1930 Congress created the Beach Erosion Control Board, a branch of the U.S. Army Corps of Engineers, and authorized it to study erosion. The Corps' role was at first limited to studies; but was expanded by the Flood Control Act of 1936, which authorized the Corps carry out erosion control projects where federal interests were involved.

After the 1954 and 1955 hurricanes, Congress directed the Corps to develop broader hurricane protective measures and authorized federal payment of 70% of the construction costs.

The March 1962 "Ash Wednesday" storm, which caused severe erosion along much of the north Atlantic seaboard and essentially destroyed the dune systems in many localities, resulted in a public outcry for more federal involvement in beach erosion control. Congress increased federal financial participation in erosion control projects to protect publicly owned beaches and shores and some privately owned beaches (primarily as demonstration projects).

Federal Flood Insurance

Congress reacted to recurring and serious erosion problems along the Great Lakes by directing the Federal Insurance Administration (FIA) to extend insurance coverage for the collapse or subsidence of land along the shore of a lake or other body of water as a result of erosion or undermining.... Standards for addressing erosion were also included in FIA guidelines for community programs. See Appendix 6-A.

To qualify, a community must prohibit man-made alteration of both sand dunes and mangrove stands within velocity zones. However, such an approach is minimal since FIA usually does not map sand dunes or mangroves as velocity areas. Coastal erosion is also not separately mapped in the FIA program nor is it normally considered in flood mapping.

Coastal Zone Management Program

The federal Coastal Zone Management Program has, since its inception in 1972, encouraged state erosion mapping, planning and regulation. In order to qualify for federal grants, state Coastal Zone Management plans are required to include the following components (CFR 023.26[1979]):

1. A method for assessing the effects of shoreline erosion;

2. Policy statements pertaining to erosion, including policies regarding preferences for nonstructural, structural or no controls;

3. A method for designating areas for erosion control, mitigation and/or restoration as areas of particular concern or areas for preservation and restoration, if appropriate;

4. Procedures for managing the effects of erosion, including nonstructural procedures; and

5. A list of legal authorities, funding programs and other techniques that can be used to meet management needs.

Coastal Barrier Resources Act

Adopted in 1982, this Act prohibits flood insurance after October 1, 1983, for all new or substantially improved structures on certain undeveloped and unprotected barriers mapped by the U.S. Department of the Interior. No new expenditures or new financial assistance were to be made available for any purpose within the mapped barrier resources system after the cutoff date, including the construction or purchase of structures, roads, airports, boat landings or bridge causeways.

Congress considered such a prohibition necessary because: "Coastal barriers serve as natural storm protective buffers and are generally unsuitable for development because they are vulnerable to hurricane and other storm damage and because natural shoreline recession and the movement of unstable sediments undermine man-made structures." (Findings of Fact, Coastal Barrier Resources Act of 1972.)

State

A number of coastal states have adopted planning and regulatory programs addressing bluff, dune and beach erosion. Some of these include:

1. **North Carolina, Michigan and Rhode Island** and have adopted 30-year erosion recession lines for bluffs and other erodable areas as part of their coastal zone regulatory programs.

2. **Rhode Island, Maine, and North Carolina** prohibit development on dunes as part of their coastal programs.

3. **North Carolina, Rhode Island, and Maine** prohibit development on beaches (See Appendix 6-B for an excerpt of the policy portion of the North Carolina Ocean Hazard Area regulation).

4. **Massachusetts** tightly regulates the removal of beach materials. An Executive Order limits public investment on beaches (see Appendix 6-C).

5. **California's** Coastal Commission has adopted guidelines for bluff top development which require stringent erosion control measures for new development on bluff tops to assure stability (see Appendix 6-D).

Local

A number of local communities have adopted bluff, dune or erosion control ordinances. For example:

1. **Onslow, North Carolina, Avalon, New Jersey**, and many other communities, have adopted dune protection ordinances prohibiting or tightly controling dune alteration.

2. **Sanibel and Pensacola, Florida** and a number of other communities prohibit development on beaches.

Setbacks have also been established by some west coast communities in **California, Oregon and Washington** and by east coast communities in **Maine, Massachusetts, Rhode Island, New York, Maryland, North Carolina and Florida**.

OPTIONS FOR COMMUNITY ACTION

Policy and Program Elements

A community with a combined flooding and erosion problem needs a policy and program recognizing the interrelationships between erosion and flooding and establishing minimum standards for location and design of structures. This policy should consider both immediate problems and long-term issues posed by sea level rise and retreat of the shore. A policy concerning rebuilding and repair after major storm is also desirable.

A community policy and program should include the following elements:

1. A limitation on the expansion of roads, sewers and water supply to areas potentially impacted by erosion;

2. Setbacks for all new structures in erosion areas reflecting the useful life of the structures;

3. Building code or zoning provisions including anchoring and piling requirements for structures outside of the setback area which may be impacted by storm waves and erosion;

4. Dune and wetland protection provisions to preserve protective barriers;

5. Construction of erosion protective or beach nourishment works (where absolutely necessary) for existing construction;

6. Public acquisition of selected high risk areas and relocation of structures.

It is particularly important that communities should, through public utility plans, avoid new public infrastructure in rapidly eroding bluff, dune or beach areas. This policy makes sound fiscal sense for the community itself and will discourage new private construction. It is consistent with broader Congressional policies to limit infrastructure on erodable coastal barriers.

Mapping

Both erosion maps and revised flood maps are needed to properly consider combined erosion and flood problems. National Flood Insurance maps, including flood insurance rate maps prepared by FIA, traditionally do not reflect erosion.

FIA examined the possibility of mapping erosion areas in a 1977 workshop concluding that erosion mapping was impractical at that time. The workshop revealed the complexity of combined erosion and flooding problems and the difficulties encountered with mapping or insuring erosion areas.

States have made considerable progress since 1977 in determining erosion recession rates and in actually mapping erosion areas. Because of this, FIA has partially modified its policy. Flood Insurance Study contractors are now required to consider state-generated erosion and recession data where it is considered reliable. Erosion is not, per se, being mapped.

State erosion maps indicating areas of bluff, beach, or dune erosion are now available for much of the coast from a variety of state and local sources, at differing scales. Many of these maps have been prepared by state or local Coastal Zone Management Programs. Examples of innovative or comprehensive approaches include:

North Carolina's Coastal Zone Management Program studies indicate that almost 40% of the ocean frontage is subject to a long-term erosion rate of 3 feet per year or more. Based on historic shoreline records, time series air photos and field information. North Carolina has identified a 30-year erosion recession line plus the recession expected from a 100-year storm for much of the state's 320 miles of ocean frontage.

Michigan is identifying a 30-year recession line along 300 miles of high risk Lake Michigan shoreline. High risk areas have been defined to include areas with recession rates of one foot or more per year. Data includes time-sequence air photos combined with historical shoreline data and field studies.

Florida is establishing coastal construction setback lines along the Atlantic and Gulf coasts under its 1970 Beach and Shore Preservation Act. Setbacks reflect dune/bluff erosion rates calculated through a time-series model. They are based upon 100-year storm surge and include wave elevations and anticipated erosion. More than 3,400 beach profiles and about 1,200 offshore profiles have been developed. Aerial photographs are used as base maps. Raw data are stored in a computerized system. The program has developed coastal construction setback lines for all 24 coastal counties having sandy beaches fronting on the Gulf or Atlantic.

Regulations

A community can reduce combined erosion and flooding damage for bluff, dune and beach areas through a combination of setbacks and performance guidelines. If development is to be permitted in high risk areas, much of cost and responsibility for the detailed data-gathering and engineering may be shifted to developers.

The damage from *bluff erosion* can be reduced through regulations:

1. Setbacks for structures through zoning or building codes such as California has done for bluff top development,

2. Drainage codes or subdivision controls to require that surface and subsurface drainage systems be installed in bluff areas to reduce erosion and slumping;

3. Use sanitary codes to prohibit the use of septic tanks where additional sub-surface drainage may increase slumping;

4. Use grading codes, zoning or subdivision controls to prohibit the removal of sand and gravel from beaches in front of bluffs and the construction of groins and other activities which may increase beach erosion on other lands.

Figure 6-7. Coastal mangroves like these in the Florida Keys reduce the height and force of hurricane waves and reduce erosion. Source: Jon Kusler.

Figure 6-8. Reestablishing vegetation on sand dunes is critical to help keep sand in place. Beach users need to be aware of the value of dune plants.　　Source: Jon Kusler.

To reduce damage from *dune erosion*:

1. Use dune protection ordinances, zoning, grading codes or subdivision regulations to prohibit development on dunes. If development is to be permitted, require adequate engineering (pilings, etc.) to withstand waves and erosion and require reestablishment of natural vegetation. See the North Carolina statute excerpts in Appendix 6-B.

2. Use grading codes or zoning to prohibit extraction of sand from dunes, the beach or offshore bars which act as reservoirs for sands.

3. Use zoning, grading codes or special codes to prohibit vegetation removal on dunes or activities such as cattle-grazing, off-road vehicles or footpaths that may destroy natural vegetation;

4. Use zoning or special codes to prohibit the use of groins and seawalls which may increase erosion in some areas while reducing it in others.

To reduce damage from *beach erosion*:

1. Use zoning, building codes, or subdivision controls to prohibit development on beaches. If development is to occur, require adequate engineering to withstand waves and erosion;

2. Use zoning, grading codes or special regulations to prohibit extraction of sand, gravel or other materials from the beach, dunes and offshore bars. Massachusetts has prohibited removal of rocks and gravel from beaches since 1760. Restriction on the use of state and local funds were contained in a 1980 Executive Order (see Appendix 6-D).

3. Use zoning or special codes to prohibit or carefully control the use of groins, seawalls, revetments and other structures that increase erosion in one area while reducing it in another.

Some state and local examples of bluff, dune and beach regulations include:

Bluffs

California's Coastal Zone Management Act, adopted in 1972, requires that new coastal development be designed to (a) insure geologic stability and structural integrity; (b) not significantly contribute to erosion; and (c) not require a protective structure (e.g., groin) during the design life of the structure. In 1976, the California Coastal Commission adopted guidelines for implementing the Coastal Act, including a section entitled "Geologic Stability of Blufftop Development." These guidelines, included in Appendix

6-D, require a setback for development if the blufftop is deemed unstable. The developer must have geotechnical studies performed by a registered professional engineer and/or geologist. In granting a permit, the Commission may require that an applicant sign a waiver of all claim against the public for future liability or damage resulting from permission to build.

Michigan prohibits new structures in the 30-year erosion recession area along Lake Michigan under its 1970 shoreline zoning statute. Flood protection from the 100-year storm is also required. Local governments are given the option of adopting regulations meeting minimum state standards.

Racine County, Wisconsin has adopted a 100-foot setback for bluff erosion areas along Lake Michigan. Bluff areas are also being acquired. In order to better study rates and causes of erosion, a volunteer "coast watch" was created. These volunteers monitor wave heights, rain, rates of erosion and other factors.

Highland Park, Illinois regulates development on bluffs and in ravine areas near Lake Michigan and established a 50-year setback requirement.

Dunes

North Carolina requires that all barrier island communities adopt dune protection ordinances. North Carolina more broadly addressed flooding and erosion in its 1974 Coastal Zone Management Act, which is the most comprehensive in the nation. Under this law, the Department of Natural Resources has established regulatory guidelines for mapped "ocean hazard" areas. Local governments are directed to regulate development consistent with these guidelines. If they fail to do so, the state will directly regulate development.

Rhode Island prohibits building in its 30-year critical erosion setback area, under its 1976 Coastal Commission Statute. The state requires a minimum construction setback of 50 feet from the shoreline, prohibits building and rebuilding on dunes, requires that new structures in high hazard areas be elevated an additional six feet in addition to storm surge elevation to allow for waves on top of flood waters, prohibits additional shoreline protection on barriers, prohibits most new building on undeveloped barriers, and requires wind protection for structures in high hazard areas.

Examples of local *dune protection* ordinances include:

East Hampton, New York was severely damaged by the 1938 hurricane. Combined coastal erosion and flooding plague this wealthy Long Island community. Some of the most expensive development in the community is located on and behind the dune system.

The community adopted a dune overlay district that includes all land within 100 feet of the dune crest. It has acquired between 400 and 500 scenic easements to protect wetlands, dunes and other areas. The Nature Conservancy and the town both have active dune and wetland acquisition programs underway.

Avalon, New Jersey, a small barrier island town of 2,500 residents, adopted a dune setback line in 1970. Its aggressive dune protection and reestablishment program won an Outstanding Conservation Advancement Achievement Award from the New Jersey Association of Natural Resources District in 1980. This program has involved planting of beach grass, erection of snow fences, control of foot traffic over the dunes and an active public education effort including mailing of dune protection information with its annual property tax bills.

Beaches

Most state programs addressing bluffs and dunes also tightly control development on beaches and the removal of beach materials. Other state and local regulations which apply to beach and other areas include:

Florida's Beach and Shore Preservation Act of 1970 requires that flooding, erosion and wind protection be provided for all structures seaward of its coastal construction setback line. Protection elevations must allow for wave heights (including wave runup). Buildings must be designed to withstand the impact of 140 mile per hour winds. Structures are to have limited impact on the dune/beach system. Erosion must be considered. These requirements are, in general, more stringent than FEMA's, since they take into account erosion, wave runup and the use of different approaches to surge modeling.

Massachusetts has prohibited the removal of rocks and gravel from beaches since 1760 to reduce erosion and storm damage. In 1980 Governor King adopted a barrier beach executive order tightly controlling the use of federal and state funds on barrier beaches. See Appendix 6-C.

Examples of local regulations for *beach and velocity zones* include:

Gulf Shores, Alabama. In 1979, Hurricane Frederic destroyed or damaged over 500 structures in this small barrier island community. Much of that damage was a result of combined erosion and flooding. Storm waves essentially destroyed the dune system and severely eroded pilings and slab foundations. After the storm, the community adopted revised regulations requiring deeper pilings, bracing of pilings and additional elevation to provide protection from waves. The community also purchased some damaged properties.

Pensacola Beach, Florida. This small barrier island community, located on Santa Rosa Island, has both flood and erosion problems. It was severely damaged by Hurricane Frederic. Prior to Hurricane Frederic, the community had adopted a 50-foot dune setback line. After Hurricane Frederic, the community adopted new regulations requiring increased pile dimensions for elevated structures, minimum pile embedment (five feet below mean sea level), direct tie-ins between corner pilings and roof members, windload protection requirements for at least 140 mile-per-hour winds and minimum elevation requirements of 13 feet.

Nonregulatory Actions

The principal nonregulatory actions for bluff, beach and dune areas are erosion control measures and relocation.

Erosion Control Measures

Erosion control may include both structural and nonstructural measures. To reduce erosion for *bluff* erosion areas:

1. Drain excess moisture from the site and strata susceptible to slumping through surface and subsurface drains;

2. Seal the ground surface to reduce infiltration and slumping;

3. Grade or terrace the bluff face to decrease the slope and increase stability. This is rarely practical for high bluffs. Once grading is completed, the terraced slope should be planted.

4. Stabilize the toe of the bluff through armoring or shore protection devices to reduce wave erosion and caving.

5. Build up and maintain a protective beach through beach nourishment, other techniques;

6. Construct retaining walls or grout unstable slope areas.

For *dune* areas:

1. Replant dune vegetation;

2. Encourage reestablishment of dunes through snow fence or other devices that trap sand transported to the dune area by winds, currents, waves;

3. Reconstruct dunes by mechanical means (e.g. grading, pumping, hauling).

For *beach* areas:

1. Construct bulkheads, seawalls, revetments groins;

2. Nourish the beach through pumping or hauling of sand from shore sources;

The potential impacts of proposed remedial measures to control coastal erosion should be carefully studied before constructing bulkheads, seawalls, groins or other engineering works. These measures have been criticized for exacerbating erosion in adjacent areas and causing environmental damage. They are temporary and costly. They increase the beach profile and raise wave heights during storms. Nevertheless, they may be the only practical approach to protect existing structures in some situations.

A number of states, including Maryland and New Jersey, have beach erosion control programs. Some federal funds are available on a cost-share basis for various types of erosion control works including groins, bulkheads and beach nourishment. Most federal programs are available to protect public areas but some funding is also available for private protection. Technical and planning assistance and financial help are also available in from some state beach erosion control programs.

Acquisition and Relocation

Public acquisition of undeveloped beach front areas for parks and other public purposes is often desirable. Acquisition can protect dunes, mangroves and natural protective barriers while preventing hazardous development.

Acquisition can be especially appropriate after flood disasters. Cituate, Massachusetts and Gulf Shores, Alabama relocated damaged structures with assistance by FEMA's Section 1362 relocation program. The key to taking advantage of post-disaster opportunities is pre-disaster planning.

Avalon, New Jersey and Sanibel, Florida are preparing pre-storm plans to guide rebuilding, acquisition and other mitigation measures after the next disaster. This is a sensible approach and will yield long-term benefits.

Appendix 6-A. FEMA Guidelines for Community Regulations. CFR, Title 44 Emergency Management and Assistance Chapter 60.5 (1980).

60.5 Floodplain management criteria for flood-related erosion-prone areas. The administrator will provide the data upon which floodplain management regulations for flood-related erosion-prone areas shall be based. If the Administrator has not provided sufficient data to furnish a basis for these regulations in a particular community, the community shall obtain, review and reasonably utilize data from the Administrator. However, when special flood-related erosion hazard area designations have been furnished by the Administrator they shall apply. The symbols defining such special flood-related erosion hazard designations are set forth in part 64.3 of this subchapter. In al cases the minimum requirements governing the adequacy of the flood plain management regulations for flood-related erosion-prone areas adopted by a particular community depend on the amount of technical data provided to the community by the Administrator. Minimum standards for communities are as follows:

(a) When the Administrator has not yet identified any area within the community as having special flood-related erosion hazards, but the community has indicated the presence of such hazards by submitting an application to participate in the Program, the community shall:

(1) Require the issuance of a permit for all proposed construction, or other development in the area of flood-related erosion hazard, as it is known to the community;

(2) Require review of each permit application to determine whether the proposed site alterations and improvements will be reasonably safe from flood-relater erosion and will not cause flood-related erosion hazards or otherwise aggravate the existing flood-related erosion hazard; and

(3) If a proposed improvement is found to be in the path of flood-related erosion or to increase the erosion hazard, require the improvement to be relocated or adequate protective measures to be taken which will not aggravate the existing erosion hazard.

(b) When the Administrator has delineated Zone E on the community's FIRM, the community shall:

(1) Meet the requirements of paragraph (a) of this sections; and

(2) Require a setback for all new development from the ocean, lake, bay, riverfront or other body of water, to create a safety buffer consisting of a natural vegetative or contour strip. This buffer will be designated by the Administrator according to the flood-related erosion hazard and erosion rate, in conjunction with the anticipated "useful life" of structures, and depending upon the geologic, hydrologic, topographic and climatic characteristics of the community's land. The buffer maybe used for suitable open space purposed, such as for agricultural, forestry, outdoor recreation and wildlife habitat areas, and for other activities using temporary and portable structures only.

Appendix 6-B: Excerpts of the North Carolina Ocean Hazard Area Regulations.

North Carolina Ocean Hazard Areas

The ocean hazard system identified by the Department of Natural Resources includes three components: (1) an "ocean erodible zone," which runs from the mean water landward equal to 30 times the long-term annual erosion rate plus the recession expected in a 100-year storm; (2) a "high hazard flood area" defined to include open coasts subject to wave action and flooding in a 100-year storm; and (3) inlet hazard areas defined through statistical analysis of past inlet movement.

A stringent minimum ocean setback is imposed, which requires that development be located behind the furthest landward of four points: (1) 30 times the long-term annual erosion rate, measured from the vegetation line; (2) the crest of the "primary" dune (defined as the first dune with an elevation equal to the 100-year storm level plus six feet); (3) the landward toe of the frontal dune (defined as the first dune with sufficient height, continuity, configuration, and vegetation to offer protective value); or (4) 60 feet, measured from the vegetation line.

.0302 SIGNIFICANCE OF THE OCEAN HAZARD CATEGORY

(a)   The primary causes of the hazards peculiar to the Atlantic shoreline are the constant forces exerted by waves, winds, and currents upon the unstable sands that form the shore. During storms, these forces are intensified and can cause significant changes in the bordering landforms and to structures located on them. Hazard area property is in the ownership of a large number of private individuals as well as several public agencies and is used by a vast number of visitors to the coast. Ocean hazard areas are critical, therefore, because of both the severity of the hazards and the intensity of interest in the areas.

(b)   The location and form of the various hazard area landforms, in particular the beaches, dunes and inlets, are in a permanent state of flux, responding to meteorologically induced changes in the wave climate. For this reason, the appropriate location of structures on and near these landforms must be reviewed carefully in order to avoid their loss or damage. As a whole, the same flexible nature of these landforms which presents hazards to development situations immediately on them offers protection to the land, water, and structures located landward of them. The value of each landform lies in the particular role it plays in affording protection to life and property. Overall, however, the energy dissipation and sand storage capacities of the landforms are most essential for the maintenance of the landforms' protective function....

.0303 MANAGEMENT OBJECTIVE OF OCEAN HAZARD AREAS

(a)   The CRC recognizes that absolute safety from the destructive forces indigenous to the Atlantic shoreline is an impossibility for development located adjacent to the coast. The loss of life and property to these forces, however, can be greatly reduced by the proper location and design of shoreline structures and by care taken in prevention of damage to natural protective features particularly primary and frontal dunes. Therefore, it is the CRC's objective to provide management policies and standards for ocean hazard areas that serve to eliminate unreasonable danger to life and property and achieve a balance between the financial, safety, and social factors that are involved in hazard area development.

(b)   The purpose of these regulations shall be to further the goals...with particular attention to minimizing losses to life and property resulting from storms and long-term erosion, preventing encroachment of permanent structures on public beach areas, and reducing the public costs of inappropriately sited development.

Appendix 6-C: Commonwealth of Massachusetts, Executive Order 181, 1980, Barrier Beaches.

<u>Preamble</u>

A barrier beach is a narrow low-lying strip of land generally consisting of coastal beaches and coastal dunes extending roughly parallel to the trend of the coast. It is separated from the mainland by a narrow body of fresh, brackish, or saline water or marsh system. It is a fragile buffer that protects landward areas from coastal storm damage and flooding.

The strenth of the barrier beach system lies in its dynamic character; its ability to respond to storms by changing to a more stable form. Frequently man induced changes to barrier beaches have decreased the ability of landform to provide storm damage prevention and flood control.

Inappropriate development on barrier beaches has resulted in the loss of lives and great economic losses to residents and to local, state and federal governments. The taxpayer, who often cannot gain access to barrier beach areas, must subsidize disaster relief and flood insurance for these high hazard areas.

Since barrier beaches are presently migrating landward in response to rising sea level, future storm damagte to development located on the barriers in inevitable.

WHEREAS, the Commonwealth seeks to mitigate future storm damage to its barrier beach areas;

NOW, THEREFORE, I, Edward J. King, Governor of the Commonwealth of Massachusetts, by virtue of the authority vested in me by the Constitution and the laws of the Commonwealth, do hereby order and direct all relevant state agencies to adopt the following policies:

1. Barrier beaches shall be given priority status for self-help programs and this priority status shall be incorporated into the Statewide Outdoor Comprehensive Recreation Plan. The highest priority for disaster assistance funds shall go towards relocating willing sellers from storm damaged barrier beach areas.

2. State funds and federal grants for construction projects shall not be used to encourage growth and development in hazard prone barrier beach areas.

3. For state-owned barrier beach property, management plans shall be prepared which are consistent with state wetland policy and shall be submitted to the Secretary of Environmental Affairs for public review under the provisions of the Massachusetts Environmental Policy Act.

4. At a minimum, no development shall be permitted in the velocity zones or primary dune areas of barrier beaches identified by the Department of Environmental Quality Engineering.

5. Coastal engineering structures shall only be used on barrier beaches to maintain navigation channels at inlets and then only if mechanisms are employed to ensure that downdrift beaches are adequately supplied with sediment.

6. Dredge material of a compatible grain size shall be used for barrier beach nourishment, if economically feasible.

7. The Coastal Zone Management Office shall coordinate state agency management policy for barrier beach areas.

Appendix 6-D: California Coastal Commission Statewide Interpretive Guidelines. Adopted 1977.

Geological Stability of Blufftop Development

Section 30253 of the 1976 Coastal Act provides that "new development shall: (1) Minimize risks to life and property in areas of high geologic, flood and fire hazard; (2) Assure stability and structural integrity, and neither create nor contribute significantly to erosion, geologic instability, or destruction of the site or surrounding area or in any way require the construction of protective devices that would substantially alter natural land-forms along bluffs and cliffs." Section 30251 provides that: "Permitted development shall be sited and designed...to minimize the alteration of natural landforms..."

A bluff or cliff is a scarp or steep face of rock, decomposed rock, sediment or soil resulting from erosion, faulting, folding or excavation of the land mass. The cliff or bluff may be simple planar or curved surface or it may be steplike in section. for the purposes of this guideline, "cliff" or "bluff" is limited to those features having vertical relief of ten feet or more, and "seacliff" is a cliff whose toe is or may be subject to marine erosion. "Bluff edge" or "cliff edge" is the upper termination of a bluff, cliff or seacliff. When the top edge of the cliff is rounded away from the face of the cliff as a result of erosional processes related to the presence of the steep cliff face, the edge shall be defined as that point nearest the cliff beyond which the downward gradient of the land surface increases more or less continuously until it reaches the general gradient of the cliff. In a case where there is a steplike feature at the top of the cliff face, the landward edge of the topmost riser shall be taken to the cliff edge.

To meet the requirements of the act, bluff and cliff developments must be sited and designed to assure stability and structural integrity for their expected economic life-spans while minimizing alteration of natural landforms. Bluff and cliff developments (including related storm runoff, foot traffic, site preparation, construction activity, irrigation, waste water disposal and other activities and facilities accompanying such development) must not be allowed to create or contribute significantly to problems of erosion or geologic instability on the site or on surrounding geologically hazardous areas.

Alteration of cliffs and bluff tops, faces, or bases by excavation or other means should be minimized. Cliff retaining walls should be allowed only to stabilize slopes, or sea walls at the toe of seacliffs or to check marine erosion where there is no less environmentally-damaging alternative and when required:

1. to maintain public recreational areas or necessary public services (such as protection of coastal highways or energy facility) or to protect port areas;

2. to protect principle structures in existing developments that are in danger from erosion; or

3. in Los Angeles, Orange, and San Diego Counties, to infill small sections of wall in subdivisions where a predominant portion of a wall is already in place, provided that such infilling would have no substantial adverse environmental effects.

A geologic investigation and report will be required when a development is proposed to be sited within the area of demonstration as defined below.

As a general rule, the area of demonstration of stability (Illustration A) includes the base, face and top of all bluffs and cliffs. The extent of the bluff top considered should include the area between the face of the bluff and a line described on the bluff top by the intersection of a plane included at a 20 degree angle from horizontal passing through the toe of the bluff or cliff, or 50 feet inland from the edge of the cliff or bluff, whichever is greater. However, the Commission may designate a lesser area of demonstration in specific areas of known geologic stability (as determined by adequate geologic evaluation and historic evidence) or where adequate protective works already exist. The Commission may designate a greater area of demonstration or exclude development entirely in areas of known high instability.

The report should indicate the location of the cliff or bluff edge, the toe of the cliff or bluff and other significant geologic features by distance from readily identified fixed monuments such as the centerline of the road nearest the bluff or cliff.

The applicant for a permit for blufftop development should be required to demonstrate that the area of demonstration is stable for development and that the development will not create a ecologic hazard or diminish the stability of the area. The applicant should file a report evaluating the geologic conditions of the site and the effect of the development prepared by a registered geologist or professional civil engineer with expertise in soils or foundation engineering, or by a certified engineering geologist. The report should be based on an on-site investigation in addition to a review of the general character of the area. Where there is a dispute over the adequacy of the report, the Commission may request that the report be reviewed by a state geologist from the Division of Mines and geology, the costs of that review and any necessary site inspections to be borne by the applicant. The report should consider, describe and analyze the following:

1. cliff geometry and site topography, extending the surveying work beyond the site as needed to depict unusual geomorphic conditions that might affect the site;

2. historic, current and forseeable cliff erosion, including investigation of record land surveys and tax assessment records in addition to the use of historic maps and photographs where available and possible changes in shore configuration and sand transport;

3. geologic conditions, including soil, sediment and rock types and characteristics in addition to structural features, such as bedding, joints, and faults;

4. evidence of past or potential landslide conditions, the implications of such conditions for the proposed development; and the potential effects of the development on landslide activity;

5. impact of construction activity on the stability of the site and adjacent area;

6. ground and surface water conditions and variations, including hydrologic changes caused by the development (i.e. introduction of sewage effluent and

irrigation water to the ground water system; alterations in surface drainage);

7. potential erodibility of site and mitigating measures to be used to ensure minimized erosion problems during and after construction (i.e. landscaping and drainage design);

8. effects of marine erosion on seacliffs;

9. potential effects of seismic forces resulting from a maximum credible earthquake;

10. any other factors that might affect slope stability.

The report should evaluate the off-site impacts of development (e.g. development contributing to geological instability on access roads) and the additional impacts that might occur due to the proposed development (e.g. increased erosion along a footpath). The report should also detail mitigation measures for any potential impacts and should outline alternative solutions. The report should express a professional opinion as to whether the project can be designed so that it will neither be subject to nor contribute to significant geologic instability throughout the lifespan of the project. The report would use a currently acceptable engineering stability analysis method and should also describe the degree of uncertainty of analytical results due to assumptions and unknowns. The degree of analysis required should be appropriate to the degree of potential risk presented by the site and the proposed project.

In areas of geologic hazard, the Commission may require that a development permit not be issued until an applicant has signed a waiver of all claims against the public for future liability or damage resulting from permission to build. All such waivers should be recorded with the County Recorder's Office.

SELECTED REFERENCES ON COASTAL FLOODING AND EROSION

Assessment of Research of Natural Hazards Staff, 1973, *Coastal Erosion Report.* University of Colorado, Boulder, Colorado.

Association of State Floodplain Managers, 1983, *Preventing Coastal Flood Disasters: The Role of the States and Federal Response*, Proceedings of a National Symposium, Ocean City, Maryland, May 23-25, 1983. Natural Hazards Research and Applications Information Center Special Publications #7. Boulder, Colorado: University of Colorado.

Balsillie, J.H., D.E. Athos, H.N. Bean, R.R. Clark, and L.L. Ryder, 1983, *Florida's Program of Beach and Coast Preservation.* In: Association of State Floodplain Managers, Preventing Coastal Flood Disasters. University of Colorado, Boulder, Colorado.

Brown, A.J., 1983, *California Coastal Storms, January-March 1983.* In: Association of State Floodplain Managers, Preventing Coastal Flood Disasters. University of Colorado, Boulder, Colorado.

Clark, J., 1980, *Coastal Environmental Management--Guidelines for Conservation of Resources and Protection Against Storm Hazards.* The Conservation Foundation, Washington, D.C.

Clayton, G.R., 1983, *Massachusetts' Coastal Floodplain Management Policy.* In: Association of State Floodplain Managers, Preventing Coastal Flood Disasters. University of Colorado, Boulder, Colorado.

Division of Land Resource Management Programs, 1979, *The Shorelands Protection and Management Act.* Michigan Department of Natural Resources, East Lansing, Michigan.

Dolan, R., B. Hayden and H. Lins, 1980, *Barrier Islands.* American Scientist, 68(1): 16-25.

Federal Insurance Administration, 1977, *National Flood Insurance Program.* Proceedings of the National Flood Insurance Program Conference on Coastal Erosion. Federal Insurance Administration, Washington, D.C..

Gilman, C., 1983, *Monitoring and Enforcement of the National Flood Insurance Program Regulations in New Jersey Coastal and Barrier Island Municipalities.* In: Association of State Floodplain Managers, Preventing Coastal Flood Disasters. University of Colorado, Boulder, Colorado.

Great Lakes Basin Commission, Standing Committee on Coastal Zone Management, 1975, *Proceedings of the Recession Rate Workshop.* Ann Arbor, Michigan: Great Lakes Basin Commission.

------, Undated, *The Role of Vegetation in Shoreline Management.* Ann Arbor, Michigan: Great Lakes Basin Commission.

Hanson, S.N., J.S. Perry and W. Wallace, 1976, *Great Lakes Shore Erosion Protection.* Madison, Wisconsin: Wisconsin Coastal Zone Management Program.

Hildreth, R., 1980, *Legal Aspects of Coastal Hazards Management.* In: Coastal Zone '80, Proceedings of a Conference. New York: American Society of Civil Engineers.

Hoffman, J., D. Keyes and J. Titus, 1983, *Projecting Sea Level Rise: Methodology, Estimates to the Year 2100, and Research Needs.* U.S. Environmental Protection Agency Washington, D.C..

Jannereth, M.R., 1983, *Michigan's High Risk Erosion Areas Program.* In: Association of State Floodplain Managers, Preventing Coastal Flood Disasters. University of Colorado, Boulder, Colorado.

Joint FRC-GLBC Task Force for Great Lakes Shorelands Damage Reduction, 1974, *A Strategy for Great Lakes Shoreland Damage Reduction.* Federal Regional Council, Chicago, Illinois.

Kuna, T., 1980, *Soft Engineering Alternatives for Shore Protection.* In: Coastal Zone '83. Proceedings of a Conference. American Society of Civil Engineers, New York.

Kusler, J.A., et al., 1971, *Regulation of Flood Hazard Areas to Reduce Flood Losses,* Vol. 1, U.S. Government Printing Office, Washington, D.C.

--------, 1972, *Regulation of Flood Hazard Areas to Reduce Flood Losses,* Vol. 2. U.S. Government Printing Office, Washington, D.C.

--------,1984, *Regulation of Flood Hazard Areas to Reduce Flood Losses,* Vol. 3. U.S. Government Printing Office, Washington, D.C.

Magoon, O. and H. Converse (editors), 1983, *Coastal Zone '83.* Proceedings of the Third Symposium on Coastal and Ocean Management. American Society of Civil Engineers, New York.

McCarthy, R. and L. Tobin, 1983, *Blufftop Regulatory Setbacks--A Regulatory Impossibility?* In: Magoon, O. and H. Converse (eds.), Coastal Zone '83. American Society of Civil Engineers, New York.

Michigan Water Resources Commission, 1970, *Great Lakes Shoreland Management and Erosion Damage Control for Michigan.* Michigan Dept. of Natural Resources, East Lansing, Michigan.

Miller, H. Crane, 1977, *Coastal Flood Hazards and the National Flood Insurance Program.* U.S. Department of Housing and Urban Development. Federal Insurance Administration, Washington, D.C..

Moore, J.W., and D.P. Moore, 1980, *The Corps of Engineers and Coastal Engineering, A 50 Year Retrospective.* In: Coastal Zone '80. Proceedings of a Conference. American Society of Civil Engineers, New York.

Moul, R.D., 1983, *Management Options: Can We Protect Our Coastal Barriers?* In: Association of State Floodplain Managers, Preventing Coastal Flood Disasters. University of Colorado, Boulder, Colorad.

Neal, W.J., O.H. Pilkey, Sr. and O.H. Pilkey, Jr., 1978, *From Currituck to Calabash: Living with North Carolina's Barrier Islands,* North Carolina Science and Technology Research Center, Research Triangle Park, North Carolina.

Nordstrom, K.F. and N.P. Psuty, 1978, *Coastal Dunes Dynamics: Implications for Protection of Shorefront Structures.* New Jersey Center for Coastal and Environmental Studies. Rutgers University, Camden, New Jersey.

-----1983, The Value of Coastal Dunes as a Form of Shore Protection in California, U.S.A. In: *Coastal Zone '83.* Proceedings of a Conference. American Society of Civil Engineers, New York.

O'Donnell, A.J., 1976, Drawing the Line at the Oceanfront. *The Role of Coastal Construction Set-Back Lines in Regulating Development of Florida's Coastal Zone.* University of Florida, Gainesville, Florida.

Owens, D., 1983, *Managing Development in Coastal Hazard Areas: State-Federal Relations.* In: Association of State Floodplain Managers, Preventing Coastal Flood Disasters. University of Colorado, Boulder, Colorado.

Penland, S., D. Nommedal and W. Schram, 1980, *Hurricane Impact on Dauphin Island.* In: Coastal Zone '80. Proceedings of a Conference. American Society of Civil Engineers, New York.

Pilkey, O.H., Sr., O.H. Pilkey, Jr., and R. Turner, 1975, *How To Live With An Island.* North Carolina Dept. of Natural Resources and Community Development, Raleigh, North Carolina.

Purpura, J., and W. Sensabaugh, 1974, *Coastal Construction Setback Line.* Florida Cooperative Extension Service, Marine Advisory Program, Tallahassee, Florida.

Standing Committee on Coastal Zone Management, 1975, *Proceedings of the Recession Rate Workshop.* Great Lakes Basin Commission, Ann Arbor, Michigan.

Streigl, A., no date, *Shoreland and Floodplain Zoning Along the Wisconsin Shore of Lake Michigan.* Wisconsin Department of Natural Resources, Madison, Wisconsin.

Szuwalski, A. and L. Clarke, 1980, *Bibliography of Publications of the Coastal Engineering Research Center and the Beach Erosion Board.* U.S. Army Corps of Engineers, Coastal Engineering Research Center, Fort Belvoir, Virginia.

U.S. Army Corps of Engineers, 1966, *Shore Protection Planning and Design.* Technical Report No. 3, 3rd ed. U.S. Army Coastal Research Center, Washington, D.C..

--------, 1970, *Shore Protection Program.* Department of the Army, Washington, D.C..

--------, 1971, *Report on the National Shoreline Study*, Department of the Army, Washington, D.C..

--------, 1973, *General Design Memorandum Phase I Hurricane --Wave Protection, Beach-Erosion Control, Brunswick County, North Carolina.* Wilmington District, Corps of Engineers, Wilmington, North Carolina.

White, G. et. al., 1976, *Natural Hazard Management in Coastal Areas.* U.S. Dept. of Commerce, National Oceanic and Atmospheric Administration, Office of Coastal Zone Management, Washington, D.C..

CHAPTER 7: FLASH FLOOD AREAS

THE HAZARD

Flash floods, as their name implies, occur quickly. Flash flooding encompasses a broad range of flood problems on alluvial fans, in narrow and steep valleys, along drainage courses in urban settings, below unsafe dams and behind unsafe or inadequate levees, and upom release of ice jam flooding. In these situations, flood waters not only rise rapidly but are high velocity and contain large amounts of debris. They tear out trees, undermine buildings and bridges and scour out new channels.

The damage caused by flash floods has doubled in the last ten years. They now rank first as a cause of weather-related deaths in the United States. Over three-quarters of all Presidentially declared disasters involve flash flooding. Examples of recent flash floods with serious loss of life include:

*   February, 1972, Buffalo Creek, West Virginia. - 118 killed and hundreds of homes washed away as a dam made of coal mine waste material gave way after heavy rains.

*   June, 1972, Rapid City, South Dakota and adjacent areas - 236 dead and $100 million in property damage after a large, slow-moving thunderstorm unleashed torrents of rain on the slopes of the Black Hills.

*   July, 1976, Big Thompson Canyon, Colorado - 139 drowned and millions in property damage after a thunderstorm deluged the western third of the canyon with 12 inches of rain in less than 6 hours.

*   July, 1977, Johnstown, Pennsylvania. - 77 dead and more than $200 million in property damage when violent thunderstorms caused up to 11 inches of rain to fall in a 7-county area over 9 hours. This contributed to the failure of several dams which compounded the stream flooding and accounted for 44 of the deaths.

*   September, 1977, Kansas City, Missouri. and adjacent areas - 25 killed and $90-million in property damage when thunderstorms turned several streams into raging torrents, such as the "gentle" Brush Creek, which flows through the heart of Kansas City.

*   November, 1977, Taccoa, Georgia. - 40 dead, half of them children, when heavy rains ruptured an earthen dam and demolished residential structures in the valley below.

Flash flooding occurs in all fifty states. Steeply sloping valleys in mountainous areas are the most common setting, but flash flooding can also occur along small waterways in urban areas. Urban flooding is an increasingly serious problem due to removal of vegetation, placement of debris in channels, construction of culverts and bridges which constrict flood flows, paving and other replacement of ground cover by impermeable surfaces which increase runoff, and construction of drainage systems which increase the speed of runoff.

The intensity and duration of rainfall and the steepness of watershed and stream gradients are the key factors in flash flooding. Other features include the amount of watershed vegetation and natural or artificial flood storage areas and the configuration of the streambed and floodplain. In general, the more intense the rainfall -- the rate of rainfall or how much rain falls in a given period of time -- the greater the probability of flash flooding. As one might also expect, the longer it rains in a given area, the greater the probability of flooding. Stationary or slow moving thunderstorms produce the most serious flash floods because of their intensity and duration. A series of fast moving storms over a short time can also produce huge volumes of runoff.

Flash floods cause greater damage than ordinary riverine floods because of the suddenness of flooding (which may prevent evacuation), the velocity of the water and the debris load. In addition, one, two or more flood crests may occur during a flash flood when a series of fast moving storms occur. Sudden destruction of structures and washout of access routes may result in loss of life. Deaths are common when motorists underestimate the depth and velocity of flood waters and attempt to cross swollen streams.

Collectively, many small subdivisions in a stream's watershed -- not just the floodplain -- can drastically increase flash flooding. Watershed changes are often not reflected in current maps and regulations governing floodplain development, underestimating the damage potential in urban settings.

EXISTING MITIGATION EFFORTS

Flash flooding has not been separately treated in mapping, regulatory and insurance efforts of the National Flood Insurance Program (NFIP) or most state programs. Nevertheless, more than 800 local governments have adopted flash flood warning, evacuation plan-

Figure 7-1. Too close for comfort: tourist cabins in Big Thompson Canyon, Colorado housed many people who were unaware of flash flood dangers. One hundred, forty-four lives were lost in the 1978 flash flood here.   Source: Rutherford Platt.

Figure 7-2. Flash flooding repeatedly damaged campgrounds at Whitewater State Park, MN. Area is now used only for daytime activities. See further discussion in Appendix 7-B. Source: Minnesota Dept. of Natural Resources.

ning or other mitigation efforts for particular streams or reaches of streams. Often these have been adopted with state or federal assistance. Examples include San Diego and Ventura Counties; California; Brattleboro, Vermont; Lycoming County, Pennsylvania; Keene, New Hampshire; Estes Park, Colorado; and Tulsa, Oklahoma. Estes Park; Colorado; Rapid City, South Dakota; and Tulsa, Oklahoma have adopted restrictive floodplain regulations for flash flood areas. Many communities, including Denver, Colorado; Chicago, Illinois; Tulsa, Oklahoma; Austin and Dallas, Texas;and King County, Washington have adopted stormwater management regulations to require onsite detention and reduce increased runoff due to urbanization. Rapid City, South Dakota; Larimer County, Colorado and Tulsa, Oklahoma have purchased areas subject to severe flash flood problems and relocated structures.

At the federal level, the National Weather Service has prepared a list of 2000 communities with potential flash flood problems. The Service issues flash flood watches and warnings as part of its weather reporting service (See Insert). It has developed both self-help and automated warning systems for implementation at the local level including the ALERT system which uses small microcomputers. Information about this system is available from the National Weather Service. The Soil Conservation Service, The Tennessee Valley Authority, U.S. Army Corps of Engineers and U.S. Geological Survey have also provided technical assistance to states and communities in developing and implementing flash flood warning systems.

Several states have adopted their own flash flood warning systems or provide assistance to local governments:

> **Colorado** has designated canyons with flash flood potential. The State Department of Transportation has erected "Climb to Safety" signs along roads in canyons with flash flood potential.

> **Connecticut** is implementing a two-tiered flood warning system in cooperation with local governments and the weather service. This system will include statewide warnings and individual town warnings. Two towns, Norwich and Sothington have already joined the system and allocated $20,000 each. The system will involve 20 of its own rain gaging stations; 5 weather stations, and a complete radio network. Data from the National Weather Service will be combined with data from the state and local gaging efforts.

Maryland is cost-sharing in design, equipment and installation of local flood warning systems as part of the watershed management program. Warning systems must be coordinated with local response plans.

New York has developed a Prototype Local Flood Warning Plan, available from the New York Department of Environmental Conservation.

All told, considerable progress has been made in identifying flash flood prone communities and in installing warning systems. Less progress has been made in adopting evacuation plans, and other implementation measures.

OPTIONS FOR ACTION

FLASH FLOOD WATCH

there may be flooding;
stay alert;
watch for thunderstorms;
keep an eye on rivers and streams;
be ready to take necessary actions if a FLASH FLOOD WARNING is issued
or if flooding is observed.

FLASH FLOOD WARNING

there is flooding;
act at once;
move out;
go to a safe area on high ground.

Policy and Program Elements

A community with a flash flood problem should adopt a policy and program with the following elements:

1. A resolution or ordinance stating that certain flood areas are subject to special risks to life and property due to rapidly rising water and in some instances, high velocity, erosion and debris.

2. The mapping or designation of streams or drainageways with potential for rapid inundation, high velocities and erosion or debris potential.

3. Regulations for new development in flash flood areas to either prohibit such development or require that it be designed and located to withstand flash flooding and so that rapid evacuation is possible. Warning systems and evacuation plans should be required for hotels and other establishments open to the public. Where

flooding will be worsened by development in the watershed, zoning and subdivision regulations should adopt a zero excess discharge goal for stormwater runoff.

4. Implementation of flood warning systems and evacuation plans for areas with existing development. (See Appendix 7-A for an inventory of organizations to be involved.)

5. Marking of flash flood areas with "climb to safety" or other indicators of risk.

6. Implementation of flood control measures (where appropriate) including construction of levees, dikes, reservoirs.

7. Relocation of structures from truly high risk areas.

Mapping

A community should prepare maps for areas subject to flash flooding. If areas are already mapped by the NFIP, the preparation of new overlay maps may be advisable. NFIP maps indicate floodway and flood fringe boundaries but do not indicate areas with rapidly rising water, high velocity (except in floodways), debris or erosion potential. New maps may also be needed for smaller streams and drainageways which typically have not been mapped by the NFIP. In mapping flash flood areas, an inventory should also be made of specific sites where threats to private and public safety may occur in the event of a flash flood such as low road crossing at hotels, motels, houses or other structures threatened by the flood waters and having inadequate access.

A community effort to identify areas with flash flood potential can begin with the collection of historical flood data. Local residents and newspaper accounts often indicate streams or reaches of streams subject to flash flooding. Historical data can be supplemented with preliminary watershed surveys based upon topographic maps, soils maps, and air photos. High gradient streams in areas of steep topography with limited vegetation or natural detention areas are often potential flash flood areas.

If sufficient funds are available, more detailed engineering studies can be used to identify streams and reaches of streams with flash flood potential, areas along these streams subject to potential debris and erosion problems or areas where threats to public or private safety may occur.

Stormwater runoff models are available to identify flash flood areas in urban settings. See the selected reference for a description of some models. In general, these models require slope, soil and land use information. Regional streamflow and precipitation as well as other data can often be obtained from published sources.

Regulation

New floodplain regulations should be adopted for existing community floodplain regulations upgraded for flash flood areas. After a flood disaster, moratoria on rebuilding can be adopted to permit mapping, planning, relocation and other mitigation. Such moratoria were adopted by both Rapid City after the 1972 flood and Larimer County after the 1976 flood in Big Thompson Canyon. Other options in both pre- and post-flood contexts include:

1. *Zoning* can be used to broaden floodways to include areas where the rapid rise of water may threaten life, areas subject to high velocity flows (if such areas are not already included) and areas subject to severe erosion. Alternatively, additional building setbacks or open space zoning can be applied to such high risk areas.

2. *Building codes and zoning* can require that buildings be designed to withstand anticipated velocities, erosion and debris. Storage of vehicles, mobile homes and other materials on the floodplain should also be regulated to insure adequate time is available for their removal in the event of a flash flood.

3. *Housing codes* can be used to require that owners of existing multi-family structures in high risk areas install warning systems and prepare evacuation plans.

4. *Drainage and subdivision regulations* can be used to require installation of drainage systems in subdivisions. They can also be used to reduce increases in runoff due to urbanization by limiting development densities and percentages of impermeable surfaces and by requiring onsite detention and flood storage areas.

5. *Land and water conservation regulations* can be adopted in rural areas to guide management of farming and forestry practices which may increase runoff.

For both urban and rural areas performance standards should be adopted for:

-- Vegetation changes or removal. On steep slopes vegetation should not be disturbed; elsewhere vegetation may be removed if revegetation is completed within a specific period of time after construction.

-- Slope changes. Any change that shortens runoff path should be carefully evaluated for impact on flooding.

-- Impervious surfaces. Impervious surfaces in high risk watersheds should be kept to a minimum. Regulations should allow conversion of only a small percentage of each total site.

-- Wetlands and other natural flood detention areas. Filling of natural detention areas should be prohibited. Creation of new detention areas should be required as a condition of plat approval or of a building permit.

Stormwater management models can be used to determine critical slopes and acceptable vegetation coverage and impervious surface. Dallas, TX has conducted detailed studies and mapping to develop such performance standards.

Nonregulatory Options

Principal nonregulatory options for flash flood areas include flood warning systems, evacuation plans and marking of hazard areas. Other options include relocation and engineering works such as dams, dikes and levees.

<u>Flood Warning Systems</u>

Flood warning systems can achieve a wide range of benefits outlined in tables Such systems may take several forms:

1. **Self-help** warning system. In populated watersheds, volunteers can monitor rainfall and stream levels during periods of intense rainfall. The inset describes how the self-help flash flood warning system works for communities in the Susquehanna River Basin of Pennsylvania. Many communities have adopted self-help systems with substantial reduction in flood losses in some instances. The National Weather Service provides technical assistance and training for communities establishing self-help flash flood forecasting and warning systems.

How a Self-Help Flash Flood Warning System Works.
The self-help flood warning system is activated by weather forecasts indicating the potential for heavy rain, by locally observed heavy rains, overland runoff or rising streams or by specific information from the National Weather Service. The initial alert starts a pre-planned system of observation and reporting. Volunteer rain and stream gage observers telephone a watershed coordinator who assembles their reports and calls the county or city flash flood coordinator. Using the rainfall and stream reports plus formulas, charts and graphs from the National Weather Service, the flash flood coordinator makes a flood forecast. A forecast can be made in 15 to 30 minutes after the reports are received. Observers report new rainfall and stream data every 30 to 60 minutes; flood forecasts are updated as needed. In addition to the rain and stream gage observers, stream patrols provide on-the-spot reports of conditions such as ice or debris jams and performance of dams, levees and floodfighting efforts. The flood forecasts are used to activate evacuation plans.

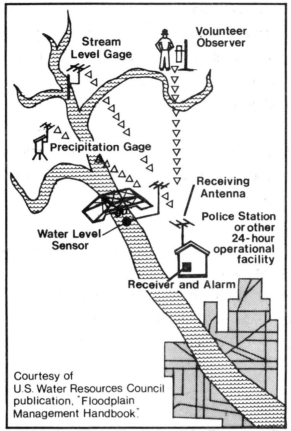

Rainfall-Flood Detection Network for the community

Figure 7-3. Elements of Automated Flash Flood Warning System.

2. **Automated flash flood warning systems.** Often, flash floods are caused by storms in remote areas -- where volunteers are not available and hired observers would be prohibitively expensive. Progress has been made in designing fully automated flash flood warning systems although few are totally operational. (See, for example, discussion of Whitewater State Park Warning System in Appendix 7-B.) Many systems use a combination of data gathered by manual and automated gaging systems. Electronic gages monitoring rainfall and stream levels feed directly into a computer programmed for flood forecasting. Many private firms now design and install automated flash flood warning systems. The National Weather Service has published specifications for communities to use when retaining a contractor to design their flood warning system.

Whether a self-help or automated system is used, flood warning and preparedness involves four major elements:

  -- a flood recognition system

  -- a flood warning arrangement

  -- a preparedness plan and

  -- maintenance arrangements.

A careful definition and coordination of roles for public service and safety organizations and the private sector are essential to the operation of each of the elements. Appendix 7-C discusses the benefits of flood warning in the 1985 flood at Ft. Wayne, IN and also shows the need for a wide variety of groups to be involved.

Emergency Response and Evacuation Plans

  Warnings can be automated; emergency response and evacuation plans cannot. A flash flood warning system is of little value without a sound emergency response and evacuation plan. Residents and visitors alike must be educated as to the correct response to a flood warning. This may include the closing of flood doors and sewer backup valves, elevation of motors and other electrical equipment, removal of rugs and personal belongings and evacuation. The map of flash flood prone areas should be prominently posted in public places. Information about the flash flood danger and about the warning systems should be discussed in the town, city, county, annual meeting. Other approaches for dissemination include local radio and television stations and brochures made available to residents and visitors.

Marking of Areas

Various types of marking may be applied to flash flood areas. After one flood, Crookston, MN posted markers on telephone poles and other public works indicating flood heights. Although this was not a flash flood, a similar approach could provide invaluable information for flash flood areas. After the Big Thompson Canyon disaster in 1976, the Colorado Department of Transportation posted "climb to safety" signs along roads in canyons along the Front Range.

Acquisition and Relocation

For areas of very high flash risk or in the aftermath of a disaster, acquisition and relocation of structures can provide a permanent solution to flash flood dangers. Relocation may be easier to promote in the aftermath of a flash flood disaster since structures are often severely damaged. Rapid City spent $45 million and purchased the entire flood-plain of Rapid Creek for open space use after the disaster in 1972.

Engineering Works

Flash floods dangers may be reduced by constructing dams and levees, floodwalls and other engineering works. However,such works may not be effective for small water-sheds with buildings at risk at many sites along the streams and drainageways.

Figure 7-4. The message on this billboard is prophetic.

Figure 7-5. The marking of flood hazard areas is a very effective public education tool. Source: Jon Kusler.

Appendix 7-A: Inventory of Public Service and Safety Organizations with Potential for or Role Related to Flood Warning and Evacuation Activities.

Organization	Leader's name	Address	Telephone number
Civil Defense			
Firemen			
Police (Municipal)			
Sheriff			
State Police			
Municipal Highway Depts.			
County Highway Depts.			
State Highway Depts.			
Hospitals, Medical Clinics			
Ambulance Service Public			
Ambulance Service Private			
Civil Air Patrol			
HAM Radio Operators			
Red Cross			
National Guard			
Other			
Other			
Other			
Other			
Other			

Appendix 7-B: Whitewater State Park -- Case Example, exepts from Minnesota Flood Pain Management Newsletter, Vol. 1, No. 2, 1983.

Whitewater State Park is a well established regional recreational area in southeastern Minnesota. In addition to the scenic bluffs, the park is a popular location for camping, hiking, fishing, swimming and cross-country skiing. Unfortunately, many of the parks facilities are located in the floodplain of the Whitewater River.

The Whitewater River has flooded on numerous occasions. Poor soil conservation practices during the late 1800's and early 1900's contributed to major flooding during the 1930's and 1940's. By the end of 1978, after four significant floods in five years, the Department of Natural Resources began to make changes in the use of floodplains in the park and explore methods of reducing the threat of floods to existing facilities.

The lack of access to the Group Camp and portions of other campgrounds was a dominant problem surfacing after each flood event in the 1970's. Unfortunately, federal disaster relief monies made available following floods in 1974 and 1975 could only be used to restore facilities to their pre-flood conditions. The need to relocate certain park facilities was recognized and incorporated into the Management Plan for Whitewater State Park.

The July, 1978 flood was the most damaging of all; federal disaster assistance exceeded $87,000. A portion of the federal relief funds was used to convert one campground to a day-use-only picnic area. State funds were later used to expand camping facilities outside of the floodplain.

The Group Camp, nestled in the narrowing valley of the Middle Fork of the Whitewater River, consists of seven cabins accommodating a total of 132 persons. The only road access to the site is over a bridge which has washed out on several occasions. The floods of 1974, 1975 and 1978 did little structural damage to these buildings. However, campers had to evacuate the area by climbing the adjacent bluffs on one occassion and were trapped in the dining hall on another occasion. Following the 1978 flood, the decision was made to close the Group Camp during the peak summer thunderstorm months until measures could be implemented to reduce the risk to human lives.

One alternative evaluated was relocating the Group Camp buildings to a site above the flood level. This alternative would have required campers to [safely] remain at the site during times of periodic flooding because the access road to the proposed site would still have been inundated by flood water. Estimates for the cost of the project approached $500,000.

Enhancing the ability to predict flood occurrences was also evaluated and ultimately chosen as the preferred alternative for two primary reasons: 1) full utilization of the Group Camp could be maintained while minimizing the threat to human safety, and 2) this alternative could be implemented at a fraction of the cost of relocating the structures.

The National Weather Service (NWS) has determined that it takes anywhere from one to five hours from the *beginning* of heavy rainfall to the flooding of the access road to the Group Camp. Past experience indicates it can take up to 20 minutes to evacuate the Group Camp. To insure to the greatest extent possible that prior warning of potential flooding is available, a three-tier approach to flood warning is now utilized in the Whitewater River valley.

First, the NWS will continue to provide advance warning of approaching storms. The NWS will issue severe weather watches and warnings directly to the park headquarters, using radio communications if necessary.

Second, an automated flood warning system was installed in the Middle Fork Whitewater River watershed. This system consists of three precipitation gages and two river level sensing gages which utilize radio telemetry to send instantaneous, "real-time" data to the park office. A microcomputer in the park office is used to receive, display and store the rainfall and river level data.

Finally, volunteers in the Whitewater River basin provide backup rainfall data in the event of hardware failure in the automated system.

Flood advisory tables, developed by the NWS, provide a means to predict whether flooding is imminent, based on antecedent soul moisture conditions and rainfall amounts. Once a decision is made that flooding is likely, a written response plan is set into action. This "Flash Flood Emergency Preparedness Plan" details actions to be taken for various anticipated levels of flooding.

While the primary beneficiary of this flood warning system is Whitewater State Park and the public it serves, much of southeastern Minnesota also benefits from this system. The NWS will have direct access to the data from this system to be used to correlate actual rainfall intensities with radar images. More accurate and timely flash flood watches and warnings should result.

Appendix 7-C: February 1985 Fort Wayne Flood Summary, excerpts from a paper by Carrol, T.R. and R.D. Marshall, 1985.

NWS Airborne Snow Survey

January, 1985 was the fifth snowiest January on record in the Fort Wayne area. From February 10 to 14, 1985, snowfall contributed to a total accumulation of 2.5 to 3.5 inches of snow water equivalent over large portions of Indiana, Michigan, and Ohio. It is interesting to note that a total snow water equivalent accumulation of 3 inches at Fort Wayne during the March 1 to 15 period has a reoccurrence interval of approximately 3300 years (U.S.DOC/WB, 1964). Soil moisture near the surface over the region was at (or above) field holding capacity. On February 15, 16, and 17 (Friday, Saturday, and Sunday), the National Weather Service made airborne snow water equivalent measurements over 92 flight lines covering 20,000 square miles in northern Indiana, southern Michigan, and northwestern Ohio.

The airborne data were sent digitally to the office in Minneapolis, checked for accuracy, entered into SHEF format, and sent over AFOS approximately one hour after the aircraft landed each noon and evening during the three day survey. In this way, the appropriate NWS offices had access to the airborne data within one hour after the aircraft landed from each survey mission.

NWS WSFO and WSO Warnings and Statements

Monday, February 18, was a government holiday. Based on the airborne data collected on February 15-17, on February 18 WSO Fort Wayne notified Allen, Adams, and DeKalb County government units that snowmelt flooding was possible for the region. On Tuesday, February 19, the Indianapolis WSFO issued a severe flood potential statement for northern Indiana. Additionally, the Indiana Governor and various state agencies were warned of the threat of severe snowmelt flooding for the northern portion of the state during the coming weekend. Weather forecasts for Thursday, February 21, called for above freezing temperatures and precipitation. WSO Fort Wayne called a meeting on February 21 with the Red Cross, Civil Defense, Lutheran Social Services, Salvation Army, Church of the Brethern and the city of Fort Wayne to warn of the flooding threat over the coming weekend. On February 25 at 1:15 PM, the Weather Service issued a crest forecast of 9.50 feet above flood stage for the Maumee River at Anthony Boulevard in Fort Wayne. Thirty-four hours and forty-eight minutes later on February 27 at 12:03 AM, the Maumee River at Anthony Boulevard in Fort Wayne crested at 9.55 feet above flood stage.

Flood Summary for 1978, 1982 and 1985

Fort Wayne has experienced substantial snowmelt flooding during the century. Major floods occurred in 1913, 1943, 1950, 1959, 1978, 1982 and 1985. The Table below summarizes the four greatest floods on the Maumee River at Anthony Boulevard in Fort Wayne where flood stage is 15 feet. It is interesting to note that although the 1978 flood crested 0.7 feet below the 1985 flood crest, the damage caused by the 1978 flood was over $50 million greater that the damage estimated for the 1985 flood by Fort Wayne officials.

FOUR GREATEST FORT WAYNE FLOODS

Year	Stage (feet)	Event (years)	Actual Damage (Feb. 1985 $)
1913	26.1	110	?
1978	23.8	25	$56.8 million
1982	25.9	77	$56.1 million
1985	24.5	50	$ 4.0 million

1982 Flood Costs

Both the U.S. Army Corps of Engineers (Detroit District) and Fort Wayne officials have estimated the 1982 flood damage cost at approximately $57 million (in February 1985 dollars). The Corps has summarized the total 1982 flood costs for each of nine major categories given in the Table below.

ACTUAL 1982 FLOOD COSTS

(Estimated by the U.S. Army Corps of Engineers,
Reconnaissance Report - June 1984)
(in February 1985 dollars)

FLOOD COSTS (Feb. 1985 $)	1982 Actual
Structure and Contents Damage	$11,138,000
Public (city and county) Costs	10,079,000
Agency Costs	2,332,000
Evacuation-Residential	1,964,000
Evacuation-Commercial	2,910,000
Lost Wages	6,370,000
Lost Business Revenue	19,943,000
Vehicle Operational Costs	743,000
Opportunity Costs for Vehicle Occupants	611,000

In response to the 1982 flood, the City of Fort Wayne produced a "Fort Wayne - Allen County Flood Protection Plan: April 1982" which outlines an 18 Month Work Program designed to minimize the impact of future flooding. The $11 million dollar program describes measures to:

1. Install river gages, prepare emergency action plans, implement an early warning system (ALERT) in cooperation with the National Weather Service, and develop a flood proofing program,

2. Build new dikes and repair and increase the height of old dikes,

3. Install backwater gates to prevent floodwater backup through the city water and sewage system,

4. Improve existing channels,

5. Acquire floodplain property,

6. Install emergency pumping stations, and

7. Prepare damage survey reports.

In addition, the National Weather Service expanded the Airborne Snow Survey Program operational flight line network to cover much of the area in Indiana, Michigan, and Ohio which experienced significant snowmelt flooding in 1982.

1985 Flood Costs

The U.S. Army Corps of Engineers Reconnaissance Report (1984) provides a procedure to estimate flood costs based on flood stage both with and without the implementation of the Fort Wayne 18 Month Work Program. Consequently, it is possible to take the 1985 flood stage and estimate what the flood damage would gave been without the implementation of the Work Program, the flood ALERT system, or the Airborne Snow Survey Program. The Table below summarizes the estimate of the 1985 flood costs without the previously mentioned improvements.

ESTIMATED 1985 FLOOD COSTS WITHOUT IMPLEMENTATION OF
THE FORT WAYNE 18 MONTH WORK PROGRAM,
THE FLOOD ALERT SYSTEM, FOR
THE AIRBORNE GAMMA RADIATION SNOW SURVEY PROGRAM

FLOOD COSTS (Feb. 1985 $)	1985 ESTIMATE
Structure and Content Damage	$8,954,000
Public (city and county) Costs	7,239,000
Agency Costs	1,681,000
Evacuation-Residential	903,000
Evacuation-Commercial	1,064,000
Lost Wages	,739,000
Lost Business Revenue	5,445,000
Vehicle Operational Costs	541,000
Opportunity Costs for Vehicle Occupants	$433,000
Total	$27,999,000

DISCUSSION AND SUMMARY

Most of the recommendations suggested in the 18 Month Work Plan were implemented before the 1985 flood. The flood ALERT system was installed and the operational airborne flight line network was established in the region before the 1985 flood. These three major improvements limited actual damage in the 1985 Fort Wayne flood to $4 million. Consequently, it is reasonable to suggest that the improvements prevented approximately $24 million in 1985 flood damage.

The Work Plan improvements which were implemented were, no doubt, responsible for preventing a major portion of the $24 million damage which would have likely occurred without the three improvements. Additionally, the flood ALERT system contributed to damage prevention by providing essential hydrometrological data required for accurate and timely flood forecasts. The airborne snow survey conducted one day after a major regional snow storm and ten days before the flood crest provided information necessary to issue an early severe flood warning for the region. The early warning facilitated timely flood fight planning and consequently contributed to the prevention of subsequent flood damage.

It is, of course, impossible to accurately partition the relative merits of each of the three major improvements implemented before the 1985 flood. It is possible, however, to arbitrarily assign various relative importances to each of the three major improvements to estimate, in a crude fashion, the contribution each improvement made to the total savings of $24 million in damage prevention. The table below gives three arbitrary estimates of the percent of the total $24 million savings associated with each of the three major improvements. In the first case, if the Work Plan contributed 80 percent to the total flood damage prevention, then the savings directly attributable to the Work Plan improvement would be approximately $19 million. In a similar fashion, the flood damage prevented as a direct result of the early warnings and river forecasts facilitated by the airborne snow survey data can be variously estimated from $700,00 to $2,400,000 depending on the relative importance placed on the airborne data.

FLOOD DAMAGE SAVINGS BASED ON IMPROVEMENT TYPE

Improvement type	Case 1		Case 2		Case 3	
18 Month Work Plan	80%	$19.2	85%	$20.4	90%	$21.6
Flood ALERT system	10%	$2.4	10%	$2.4	7%	$1.7
Airborne Snow Survey	10%	$2.4	5%	$1.2	3%	$0.7

Note: $ in millions

The $7,700 cost of the February 1985 Fort Wayne airborne snow survey was substantially less than the projected flood damage prevented as a result of the early warnings and flood forecasts based on the airborne snow water equivalent data.

SELECTED REFERENCES FOR FLASH FLOODS

Barr Engineering, Co., 1981, *Flash Flood Warning System in Minnesota*. Report prepared for the Minnesota Dept. of Natural Resources.

Barrett, C.B., 1981, *National Prototype Flash Flood Warning System*. Paper presented to the 4th Conference on Hydrometeorology, Reno, Nevada. Boston, Massachusetts: American Meteorological Society.

Barrett, C.B., 1983, *The NWS Flash Flood Program*. Paper presented to the 5th Conference on Hydrometeorology, Tulsa, OK. Boston, Massachusetts: American Meteorological Society.

Bartfeld, I. and D. Taylor, 1982, *A Case Study of a Real-Time Flood Warning System on Sespe Creek, Ventura County, California*. Proceedings from a Symposium on Storms, Floods and Debris Flows in Southern California and Arizona, 1978 and 1980. Washington, D.C.: National Academy Press.

Benson, K.K. and J. Solstad, editors, 1983, *Minnesota Flood Plain Management Newsletter*, Vol. 1, No. 2, May-July. St. Paul, Minnesota: Dept. of Natural Resources.

Carrol, T.R. and R.D. Marshall, 1985, *Cost Benefit Analysis of Airborne Gamma Radiation Snow Water Equivalent Ft. Wayne Flood*. Paper presented at 6th Conference on Hydrometeorology, Indianapolis, Indiana. Boston, Massachusetts: American Meteorological Society.

Carter, M., 1980, *Natural Hazards Warning Systems*, NHS Report Series No. 79-02. Minneapolis, Minnesota: University of Minnesota.

Hydrology Subcommittee of the Federal Interagency Advisory Committee on Water Data, 1985, *Guidelines on Community Local Flood Warning and Response Systems. Reston*, Virginia: U.S. Geological Survey.

Flood Loss Reduction Associates, 1981, *Cooperative Flood Loss Reduction: A Technical Manual for Communities and Industry*. Lewisburg, Pennsylvania: SEDA Council of Governments and the U.S. Water Resources Council.

National Advisory Committee on Ocean and Atmosphere, 1983, *The Nation's River and Flood Forecasting and Warning Service*. Spcieal Report to the President and Congress.

National Weather Service, 1977, *Guide for Flood and Flash Flood Preparedness Planning*, U.S. Dept. of Commerce, National Oceanic and Atmospheric Administration, National Weather Service. Silver Spring, Maryland: National Weather Service.

National Weather Service, no date, *Guide for Flood and Flash Flood Preparedness Planning*. Prepared for Disaster Preparedness Service by H.J. Owen.

Owen, H.J., 1982, *Flood Warning System, Does Your Community Need One?*. Prepared for the National Weather Service.

------, 1979, *Information for Local Officials on Flood Warning Systems.* Prepared for the National Weather Service.

------ and M. Weadell, 1981, *Effectiveness of Flood Warning Preparedness Alternatives*, U.S. Army Corps of Engineers Research Report 81-ROB. Fort Belvoir, Virginia: U.S. Army Corps of Engineers.

Susquehanna River Basin Commission, 1978, *Planning Guide Self - Help Flood Forecast and Warning System*, Swatara Creek, Pennsylvania, Publication 42. Harrisburg, Pennsylvania: Susquehanna River Basin Commission

------,1979, *Flood Forecast and Warning System Evaluation*, Susquehanna River Basin, New York, Pennsylvania and Maryland. Report of an Interagency Task Force prepared for the U.S. Army Corps of Engineers. Harrisburg, Pennsylvania: Susquehanna River Basin Commisssion.

CHAPTER 8: FLUCTUATING LAKE LEVELS

THE HAZARD

The shores of lakes are frequently developed without considering that water levels can and do vary greatly over time. Most people know that lake levels fluctuate daily or seasonally with rainfall and snowmelt. Lake levels can also rise dramatically - remaining high for years or even decades - in response to long-term climatic changes. Fluctuations of five to fifteen feet are not uncommon.

Fluctuating water levels are a problem with all types of lakes including the Great Lakes. Long-term fluctuations are a particular problem on lakes formed by glacial action (the majority of the nation's lakes). Flooding can be especially acute on lakes which have no outlet, water levels on these lakes are closely tied to regional ground water levels. There are perhaps more than 100,000 glacially-formed lakes in the northern tier of states (excluding Alaska).

Flooding is also a problem for lakes created by meandering stream channels. These oxbow lakes are the depressions left behind when the main channel of a river moves to a new position. Oxbow lakes are common in the floodplains of the Mississippi, its tributaries, and other southern rivers.

In the lake regions of Wisconsin, Michigan, Minnesota, New Hampshire, New York and Maine, recreational development is typically located on 50-100 foot-wide lots and within 50-75 feet of the water. Much of this development is on a rim or ridge surrounding the lake. This rim may be 3-15 feet above the mean lake level. Minor fluctuations in lake level, due to severe thunderstorms or unusually large runoff from spring snowmelt, can flood basements or first floors. Larger fluctuations of 5-15 feet due to long-term fluctuations in ground water levels can cause severe flooding.

The traditional concept of a riverine flood is that normally dry land areas adjacent to the channel are temporarily inundated by flood waters. The waters rise to a peak and then diminish as the water retreats to the channel. The whole process occurs over a period of hours or perhaps a few days. This type of flooding also occurs on lakes with adequate outlets. Flooding on lakes with no or an inadequate outlet is completely different. Here, lake levels may rise and remain high for years, even decades.

WHAT CAUSES LAKE LEVEL FLUCTUATIONS?

Water level fluctuations on lakes can be caused by both natural and man-made events. Natural factors include precipitation, evaporation, runoff, ground water, ice, aquatic growth, meteorological disturbances and, in larger lakes, tides and crustal movement. Artificial factors influencing lake levels include dredging, diversions, consumptive use of the water and regulation by structural works. The role of long-term climate trends is imperfectly understood but does play a part in defining the range of possible fluctuations.

Long-term fluctuations are the result of persistent low or high water supply conditions affecting the basin. The extremely low levels of lakes after the 1930's drought and the extremely high level of Great Salt Lake at this time are examples of long-term fluctuations. The intervals between periods of high and low levels and the length of such periods vary widely and erratically. The extreme lake levels are likely to persist even after the factors which caused them have changed.

Seasonal fluctuations reflect the annual hydrologic cycle. In the early spring, as a result of snowmelt, heavier rains and reduced evaporation over the basin, the water level begins to rise from winter low. This trend continues until the lake peaks in the summer. During the summer, more persistent winds and drier air intensify evaporation; also the runoff and ground water flow reach their lowest values. As the water supplied to the lake becomes less than the outflow, the water level begins the downward trend to winter minimum.

Short-term fluctuations are the most dramatic changes in water levels and are caused by strong winds and by sharp differences in barometric pressure. These fluctuations usually last less than one day and do not represent any changes in volume of water of the lake.

Modified from "Great Lakes Water Level Facts", U.S. Army Corps of Engineers, Detroit District.

Long duration flooding has serious implications. First, to map the 100-year floodplain is, in most cases, technically difficult or impossible if traditional methods are employed. Historical lake data, gage analyses and biological determinations based on land and aquatic vegetations are needed. Second, traditional regulatory requirements such as elevation of buildings on pilings or floodproofing of structures and utilities are inadequate since such protection approaches will not withstand years of water.

EXISTING MITIGATION EFFORTS

Floodplain management programs have rarely addressed lake flooding. Many of the glaciated states do have shoreland management programs but most of these have primarily addressed lake management from the perspective of aesthetics, water quality and recreation. Only when lake levels rise and flood structures does the need to incorporate flood damage reduction parameters become apparent.

Some communities have adopted special management programs for lakes with long-term fluctuations, for example:

Lake Pulaski, Minnesota

After 100 structures were flooded by rising lake levels, Wright County, MN, the City of Buffalo, Buffalo Township and the Minnesota Department of Natural Resources entered into a cooperative agreement to regulate and manage Lake Pulaski, a 770-acre lake west of the Twin Cities Metropolitan area (see draft of management plan, Appendix 8-A). While the complete story of this mitigation effort is quite complex and is not yet successfully concluded, many of the mapping and regulatory procedures formulated here may be applied elsewhere. See the insert on one approach to the mapping of the floodplain of a lake and Appendix 8-B)

Lake Elsinore, California

Flooding due to rains and the limited outlet of the lake is a periodic phenomenon on Lake Elsinore and has occurred at least seven times over the last 200 years. Flooding on Lake Elsinore in 1980 damaged or destroyed over 400 structures and required the removal of 450 mobile homes. The City of Lake Elsinore adopted revised floodplain regulations (see Appendix 8-C) prohibiting new development below the 100-year flood elevation unless structures are located on land. Their previous ordinance, which was in effect at the time of the flood, had allowed new structures on pilings; this had contributed to flood damage. The city has also developed a plan for acquisition of flood-prone properties to be funded by FEMA through its section 1362 program, state park acquisition and local funding sources.

The Great Lakes

Eight states of the highly industrialized North Central region border on the Great Lakes. The total area within the basin in the United States is 174,000 square miles, of which 61,000 square miles is water. Except where bedrock outcrops or where protective works have been constructed, the glacial debris comprising the shore of the Great Lakes is highly erodible.

Shore erosion and flooding have been major problems, especially in periods of high lake levels such as the late 1920's, mid 1940's, early 1950's, early 1970's and the present time. Shore property damages increase with each high water period because of further development of unprotected shorelands and continually increasing shore property values.

Figure 8-1. When these photos were taken, these homes on Lake Pulaski, Minnesota had been under water for approximately three years. See discussion in Appendix 8-A. Source: Minnesota Dept. of Natural Resources.

Most of the affected states have adopted management programs that require building standards and setbacks for new construction. There will, however, continue to be damages to existing properties, many of which are part of the public infrastructure.

Great Salt Lake, Utah

Great Salt Lake is a "terminal" lake which means it receives inflow but has no outlet. It is a remnant of Glacial Lake Bonneville which covered 20,000 square miles in Utah, Nevada and Idaho during the last Ice Age.

Since the Morman pioneers settled the valley in 1847, accounts of lake levels have been well documented. Typical fluctuations have been between 4191.55 and 4205 feet. In 1963, the lake fell to a low of 4191.35 and there were concerns that the lake would go dry. By 1975, its level had risen to 4202 and consideration was given to lowering the level by pumping water out into the desert. The level was maintained with minor fluctuations until the fall of 1982 when it began to rise in response to a series of storms. Between September 18, 1982 and June 30, 1983, the lake rose 5.2 feet; the greatest seasonal rise ever recorded. The level as of July 15, 1985 was 4209.4. Damage estimates for losses at the end of 1983 were approaching $500 million.

A solution to the problems associated with the Great Salt Lake is difficult. The economic impact on the private sector has already been tremendous. The public infrastructure has also suffered. Structural solutions, such as upstream impoundments, may not be economically or environmentally feasible. Regardless of the array of actions that are ultimately taken, a strong floodplain management program and strict land use controls need to be implemented.

OPTIONS FOR ACTION

Policy and Program Elements

Where there is potential for lake flooding problems, a policy and program with the following elements may be appropriate:

1. A policy statement or resolution that long-term fluctuations in water levels may result in flood damages quite different than those for riverine flooding;

2. A ban on roads, water and sewer extensions to areas subject to long-term inundation;

3.   A set of regulations that prohibit building in semi-permanently flooded areas. If building is to take place, it should occur only on fill with adequate access, water supply and waste disposal during times of high water;.

4.   A strategy for relocating or protecting structures in areas subject to long-term fluctuations;

5.   If the lake extends across the boundaries of more than one unit of government, a formal agreement that insures intergovernmental coordination and cooperation. The exact form of the agreement will vary with different state laws. Examples of cooperative arrangements include joint powers agreements, lake management districts and watershed districts. The management plan for Lake Pulaski, Minnesota (see Appendix 8-A) contains a comprehensive policy statement.

Mapping

Where a lake is part of a river system (e.g., a reservoir), conventional flood maps may accurately portray lake flooding. When the lake is not part of a flowage, consideration has to be given to the water budget of the lake and its watershed. Unfortunately, the climatic, soil, lake level and ground water level needed exist to make a precise analysis is rarely available. Biological and ecological characterization, historical high water remembrances, analysis of soils and analysis of landforms are alternative methods for outlining the historical lake bed and potential flooding levels.

The following insert describes how biological and geomorphic data are used to establish the Natural Ordinary High Water (NOHW) mark in Minnesota. The NOHW is the line that separates state regulations of the bed of the lake from local regulation of the shoreland. Several states have a similar mapping element although there is variation in the specific parameters.

MAPPING THE FLOODPLAIN OF A LAKE; ONE APPROACH

Resource management and riparian rights pertaining to an inland lake are dependent upon identification and establishment of that lake's Natural Ordinary High Water (NOHW) elevation. The NOHW is coordinated with the upper limit of the lake basin and defines the elevation (contour) on the lakeshore which delineates the boundary of public waters. Identification of the NOHW comes from an examination of the bed and banks of a lake to ascertain the highest water level where the presence and action of water has been maintained for a sufficient length of time to leave recoverable evidence. The primary evidence used to identify the NOHW of a lake consists of biological (vegetation) and physical features found on the banks of the lake. Data depicting historic lake levels are of-

ten useful only as supporting data in NOHW studies. This is because the available data generally are not of sufficient detail, continuity, frequency and/or length of record to alone identify the NOHW.

Because trees are the most predominant and permanent expression of upland vegetation, they are used as NOHW indicators wherever suitable species and sites can be located. Particular attention must be given to the species of upland growth selected for consideration. In general, willow and most ash are very water tolerant; maples and elms tolerant; most birch intermediately tolerant and oak intolerant. The less tolerant trees make the best indicators, but factors in addition to species also have to be considered such as age, the slope of ground, the effect of water and ice action on the shoreline and the physical condition and growing characteristics of the trees. Water dependent vegetation such as cattails will follow lake levels as they rise and fall and therefore provide little evidence about the lake's NOHW, except in cases where more permanent vegetation does not exist. Trees, like people, will follow receding water levels and infringe upon the lake basin. When water levels rise to reclaim the basin such trees are inundated and eventually die.

The tree analysis involves a relationship between the elevation of the ground at the base of the tree and the diameter of the tree. Depending upon the species of tree selected and the slope of the ground, it can be generally stated that a tree requires a depth of unsaturated soil about equal to its trunk diameter to grow. Most trees will not survive if water levels saturate their root systems for a sufficient period of time and if they do survive, stress signs may be evident in the growing characteristics of the tree. The diameter, height, shape of the stem, branch shape, branch spread and foliage density reflect the extent to which the tree roots have had an opportunity to penetrate into and spread through the soil to reach the elements that stimulate growth. A tree growing near the basin's fringe will often indicate by its general appearance whether its root system has had breathing space and sufficient nourishment and support from the soil in which it grows. As an example, a seedling started in soil six inches above a zone subject to saturation will grow normally until it reaches a diameter of approximately six inches, after which it will show by its general appearance the adverse growing characteristics mentioned above.

Physical features searched for include soil characteristics, beachlines, beach ridges, scarp or escarpment (more prominent scarp can often be found in the form of the undercutting of banks and slopes), ice ridges, natural levees, berms, erosion, deposition, debris, washed exposed shoreline boulders, high water marks, movement of deposits as a result of wave action, top and toe of bank elevations as well as water levels. Caution is taken to be aware that many of the listed geomorphological features may take a long time to develop and also that several sets of these features may be found. That is, a lake likely will have more than one stage where the action of water has left recoverable evidence, however only the stage coordinated with the upper limit of a basin is used to assist in identifying the NOHW level. As an extreme example, water level stages resulting from the drought years of the 1930's certainly were the result of natural conditions extending over a number of years, but the resulting recoverable evidence is of no use in NOHW determinations.

Credits: Excerpts from NATURAL ORDINARY HIGHWATER MARK DETERMINATION. Report for Pulaski Lake, MN. Minnesota Department of Natural Resources, Division of Waters, March 1985.

Regulations

Floodplain zoning, shoreland zoning, subdivision control, building codes, and other special codes can be used to establish:

Protection elevations. In determining protection elevations, allow substantial freeboard where there is the potential for wave action or ice damage. The amount of freeboard should be based on the fetch (open water area), anticipated wave heights, and thickness of the ice (if this is a factor).

Buffers and setbacks. Wisconsin, Minnesota, Washington and Maine require minimum setbacks of 75 feet for new structures on all lakes.

No Fill. Requirements that structures be located on land, not on fill, at an elevation above the natural high water level.

Prohibit basements. Basements can be prohibited, use of the basement as living area can be prohibited.

Sanitary codes. Sanitary codes can be used to prohibit septic systems in expected flood and high ground water areas where such systems will not function.

Well construction codes. Well construction can require proper abandonment of wells to protect ground water and can contain requirements for siting new wells.

Flood loss reduction standards are often appropriately included not only in flood hazard reduction ordinances, but also in shoreland zoning, wetland protection and broader land use controls.

Nonregulatory Actions

Acquisition and Relocation

Relocating structures may be the only practical solution when long-term flooding renders them useless. Relocation is taking place on Lake Elsinore and has been proposed for some structures on Lake Pulaski.

Outlet Construction

Efforts have been made on both Lake Elsinore and Pulaski to construct outlets, reducing water levels. The problem with this approach is that it may be difficult to find a place to put the excess water.

Levees

Levees have been constructed to reduce flooding on the Great Salt Lake. However, levees are usually a temporary solution to flood problems.

Appendix 8-A: A Management Plan for the Developed Lake Bed Area of Lake Pulaski, Wright County, Minnesota.

INTRODUCTION

Lake Pulaski is located near the center of Buffalo Township (T120N, R25W) in Wright County Minnesota. The south half of the lake is located within the corporate limits of the City of Buffalo.

A December 1981 report by the Division of Waters of the Department of Natural Resources (DNR) estimated the Natural Ordinary High Water level (NOHW) of Lake Pulaski to be at an elevation 968.8 or roughly seven feet above present levels.

On June 11, 1982, in accordance with state law and after public hearings, the Commissioner of Natural Resources signed an order officially establishing the 968.8 elevation as the NOHW of Lake Pulaski. All land located adjacent to Lake Pulaski that is below this elevation is now considered lake bed. Upon signing this order, it is estimated that roughly 100 structures are considered located on the bed of Lake Pulaski and at least 170 structures will receive some water-related damage. At the 968.8 elevation, roughly 60 acres of land that is above the present lake level would be inundated by water.

This fact presents a very unusual but not unprecedented problem in Minnesota's history of shoreline management. Several lakes in eastern Minnesota have similar problems, such as Big Marine Lake in Washington County. However, this is the first time that the DNR has established the NOHW level to be above this many residences **before** the lake reclaimed itself. Experience from these eastern lakes has shown that the combination of lakeshore owners trying to save their homes, together with conflicting and uncertain authorities of state and local governments can lead to many problems. The Lake Pulaski problem is unprecedented in the respect that this is the first time state and local governments have had the chance to prepare for the problem in advance of its becoming severe.

The City of Buffalo and Buffalo Township contracted with Zack Johnson and Associates to study the Lake Pulaski problem and to work with a local task force in making recommendations to state and local governments as to how to deal with it. The study entitled "Lake Pulaski Area Development Study" was released in July of 1982 and it explored many possible solutions to the low development problems including artificial control of the lake level, filling and raising of all the structures, acquisition of the lake bed area, relocation of homes, and adoption of development controls.

The task force which worked with Zack Johnson and Associates came up with several recommendations on how to deal with the Lake Pulaski problem. Most of these recommendations involved non-structural means of addressing the problem. That is, they concluded that artificial manipulation of the lake level and massive relocation programs were not financially feasible. Instead, they recommended use of development controls (zoning), public information, and further study as the most cost-effective way of addressing the problem. The Department of Natural Resources supports the task force's recommendations and hopes to see all of them carried out.

The purpose of this plan is to address the environmental, social, and regulatory issues involved in future management of the lake bed area of Lake Pulaski and to lay out the framework and policies which state and local governments will follow in administering the area. The purpose is also to make this information available to local residents, developers, real estate agents and particularly lake bed owners, so that they fully understand the legal limitations that govern the existing and future use of the lake bed area.

This plan is prepared under authority granted the Department of Natural Resources in Minnesota Statutes, Section 104.03 (Flood Plain Management), 105.39 (Authority of Commissioner -DNR-), 105.403 (Water and related land resources plans), 105.42 (Public water permits) and 105.48 (Shoreland management).

GEOLOGY AND HYDROLOGY

The geology and other physical characteristics of Lake Pulaski are addressed in both the "Lake Pulaski Area Development Study" and the Department's "Natural Ordinary High Water Determination for Pulaski Lake". The size of Lake Pulaski has been measured at 837 acres in 1858, 770 acres in 1953, and 786 acres in 1979. The watershed, that is all land that slopes towards Lake Pulaski, has been estimated to be roughly 3500 acres in size. This results in a 3:1 watershed to lake area ratio, which is generally considered insufficient to maintain water levels in Pulaski. Therefore, it is assumed that the levels of Pulaski are in large part affected by ground water levels and ground water inflow (commonly referred to as being "spring fed").

Since ground water inflow is extremely difficult to measure and since the extent of and recharge capabilities of the aquifers affecting Lake Pulaski are largely unknown, any calculations regarding projected levels and timing of those levels is impossible at this time. The only thing that is known for certain is that levels in Lake Pulaski reached and stayed at elevation 968.8 feet for extended periods at least once and possibly twice within the past 125 years. It should be noted that there was also evidence that the lake had exceeded 968.8 feet by 2 or 3 feet sometime in the past.

Reading of the two previously mentioned reports is recommended for those interested in more detailed information on the physical characteristics and history of Lake Pulaski.

EXISTING REGULATORY AUTHORITIES

Presently, five governmental units have some interest or authorities relating to Lake Pulaski. They are the Federal Government, State Government, Wright County, the City of Buffalo, and Buffalo Township. A summary of the general interests and authorities of each unit follows:

Federal Government:
Direct authority over placement of fill in the lake or adjoining wetlands by the U.S. Army Corps of Engineers. No direct land use authority. Some Federal interest in Pulaski problems is through financial assistance type agencies such as HUD, VA, SBA, FHA, etc. Some technical assistance available through SCS. Primarily federal interest is through the Federal Emergency Management Agency (FEMA) which administers the disaster assistance programs and the Flood Insurance Program.

State Government:
DNR - Direct authority over all activities occurring below the ordinary high water level. Indirect authority over all property located within 1000 feet of the lake, through

the Shoreland Management Program and indirect authority over all land located below any estimated 100-year flood level, through the State Floodplain Management Program. Permits are required of all individuals, companies, agencies, or government units doing any work that changes the cross-section of the bed of Lake Pulaski. Local governments are required to adopt and enforce ordinances relating to Shoreland and Floodplain areas that meet the minimum standards developed by the DNR.

Pollution Control Agency (PCA): Direct authority over water quality aspects of Lake Pulaski relating to community sewage discharge, feed lot location and construction of landfills. Indirect authority relating to individual sewage treatment systems and general ground and surface water quality.

Department of Health (DOH): Direct authority over well construction and location, and commercial food or recreation related establishments. Well drillers have to be licensed and must follow DOH well code which specifies various elevation requirements and setbacks.

Local Government

Wright County: Has extensive direct land use authority which is administered through the Wright County Planning and Zoning Ordinance. This ordinance contains provisions which meet or exceed all DNR required shoreland and floodplain provisions. This authority applies to the north one-half of the lake only. The County also has taxing authority over the area and property values of the area may affect county revenues.

City of Buffalo: Has extensive direct land use authority over the south one-half of the lake, which is administered through the City's zoning ordinance. This ordinance does not meet all of the DNR required shoreland and floodplain provisions, but the City recently enacted a moratorium on any development below the ordinary high water level. The City also has indirect control over land uses on Lake Pulaski through its municipal sewage collector system.

Buffalo Township: Has the authority to adopt extensive land use controls provided they meet or exceed the county standards. These controls would apply to the north half of the lake only. However, the township presently addresses its land use concerns through the County planning process.

The primary tool by which governmental units control uses of land is through a permit or approval system. What follows is a listing of common development activities that do or could occur in and around Lake Pulaski, and a summary of the various types of permits and/or approvals that are required for each activity.

1. Erecting, moving or wrecking any building or structure. A building permit is required by either the City of Buffalo or Wright County any time this activity occurs within their corporate boundaries. In the County, the permit may actually be issued by a Township Building Inspector, but a permit is not required for a building of less than 150 square feet of area. On the lake bed area, a permit would also be required by the DNR and possibly by the U. S. Army Corps of Engineers. Generally, DNR regulations would prohibit building or moving new structures onto the lake bed; the city or county would normally issue building permits provided the building code and all other ordinance provisions are met. On the lake bed both the City and County prohibit the construction or location of new structures.

2. _Remodeling, enlargement, repair or modification of existing structures._ A building permit is required for any of these activities either in the City or County controlled areas. On the lake bed area, DNR permits would also be required, except for minor repairs such as reshingling and painting. Under the county ordinance, lake bed structures are classified as a nonconforming use which cannot be extended or expanded. However, the county ordinance does allow normal maintenance of structures. The City does not differentiate between lake bed or non-lake bed areas.

3. _Filling, excavation, landscaping, terracing, grading, and construction of retaining walls._ On the lake bed area, these activities all require a permit from the DNR. Whether or not such permits are issued depends on the environmental effects and the purpose of the activity. Permits from the U. S. Army Corps of Engineers are generally needed when material is placed in the lake bed, but not for excavation. In the county controlled lake bed area, placement of fill requires a conditional use permit, which can be issued if the applicant can show that the fill has some beneficial purpose and the amount is as small as possible. Outside of the lake bed area, but within the county controlled shoreland area, a land alteration permit is required any time more than 50 cubic yards of earth is to be moved. Within city controlled lake bed and shoreland areas, a specific permit is not required for any of these activities but they may be controlled by the City when done in conjunction with another controlled activity.

4. _Subdivision of land._ In the County controlled area any division of property or moving of lot lines requires approval of the County. Simple lot line adjustments are handled through the Board of Adjustment. Division of tracts of land for development requires that platting procedures be followed and requires County Board of Commissioner's approval. Within the City, any time property is divided into parcels smaller than 2 and one-half acres in size or 150 feet in width, platting provisions must be followed and City Council approval is required.

5. _Installation, repair, replacement, removal or use of individual on-site sewage treatment systems._ Within the County controlled area, a permit is required prior to installation, alteration or repair of any individual on-site sewage disposal system. On the lake-bed area, a DNR permit may also be required as such installation or repair would involve a temporary or permanent change of the cross-section of the bed of the lake. Within the City, on-site systems are prohibited and hook up to public sewer is required.

RECOMMENDED POLICIES AND REGULATORY CHANGES

From reading the preceding section, one can see that the authority of the federal, state, and local government units often overlap as regards control of the lake bed area. In examining the various policies relating to each of the involved permit requirements, it becomes obvious that none of the affected regulations or ordinances were really designed to deal with this unique situation. Therefore, it is felt that some general policies must first be agreed upon by the state and local governments, before the regulatory conflicts can be sorted out. These recommended policies and the action needed to implement the policies follow:

1. *Policy* - Existing structures located on the lake bed may remain in their present location and continue their present level of use until water levels make their habitation unsafe.

Action - The State, County and City shall implement a monitoring program in order to notify owners when continued habitation of their homes could be hazardous.

2. *Policy* - Existing structures on the bed may be repaired or maintained provided the degree of permanence of the structure and the outside dimensions of the structure are not increased. Permits for such repair or modification shall be required by the County and City in conformance with existing ordinances or codes.

Action - The DNR shall issue general permits to both the County and City so that lake bed owners only have to deal with one agency. These general permits would only apply if the above policy was met.

3. *Policy* - Existing structures on the lake bed shall comply with on-site sewage treatment standards. Those whose systems are polluting shall be encouraged to install temporary holding tanks or to find a disposal site out of the lake bed.

Action - The City should require city sewer hook-up for any homes not presently served by such. The County should consider the issuance of variances to allow temporary holding tanks to be utilized. The DNR will not require permits for either of these activities provided adequate conditions are placed on the local permits to prevent future pollution and to assure removal of the tank or disconnection from the system when appropriate.

4. *Policy* - Fill for lots that are totally surrounded by lake bed shall be prohibited. Fill for lots that connect to land above the bed may be issued provided that certain conditions are met. Fill to raise public roads leading to lake bed lots shall be prohibited unless the lots are connected to land above the bed.

Action - DNR shall institute the above policy in compliance with the Public Waters Permits Standards. The County and City should adopt a policy to not take any actions that encourage filling that would not be allowed under this policy.

5. *Policy* - New or additional structures shall be completely prohibited from being located on the lake bed. The reuse or reoccupation of lake bed lands shall be in conformance with all state and local standards.

Action - None necessary

6. *Policy* - Temporary flood fighting measures such as sandbagging, pumping, or dike construction should be discouraged. However, pumping and sandbagging should not be strictly prohibited unless it is obvious that they will become permanent features of the lake bed.

Action - Agreement by the State, County and City regarding enforcement policy should be made.

7. *Policy* - The "Management Plan" for Lake Pulaski shall be utilized to effectuate a long-term solution for high water problems.

Action - The state shall develop specific rules for dealing with future development and reuse of lake bed lands. The County and the City should consider similar specific rules or guidelines for lake bed lands. In addition, the State, County and City should cooperate in joint administrative actions to implement the "actions" recommended in the Management Plan.

RECOMMENDED LONG-TERM APPROACHES

As the lake level rises, there is no doubt that considerable new interest will again develop in things such as lake level control structures, dikes, relocation funding. Before any of these activities are again explored, it is recommended that all efforts be directed towards obtaining funding to study the lake and ground water hydrology in much detail. Dikes and lake level control could not even be considered without this information. Also such information would be extremely useful in timing any relocation efforts and in making sure that any relocated homes are placed at a high enough level.

At this point in time, it appears that the best and most cost-effective long-term solution would be relocation. Several home owners already have or are in the process of doing so on their own. Also, relocation may also be at least partly accomplished through the Federal Flood Insurance Program, as many of these landowners already have flood insurance coverage.

Appendix 8-B: Minnesota Department of Natural Resources, Conservation Regulations. Standards for Local Government Regulation of Shoreland Areas

4.22 High Water Elevation
In addition to the setback requirements of Section 4.21:

For lakes, ponds or flowages: No structure, except boat houses, piers and docks, shall be placed at an elevation such that the lowest floor, including basement floors, is less than three feet above the highest known water level. In those instances where sufficient data on known high water levels are not available, the elevation of the line of permanent shoreland vegetation shall be used as the estimated high water elevation. When fill is required to meet this elevation, the fill shall be allowed to stabilize, and construction shall not begin until the property has been inspected by the Zoning Administrator.

Appendix 8-C: Ordinance Prohibiting Construction, Additions and Alterations of Buildings at or below Certain Levels.

ORDINANCE No. 604

AN ORDINANCE OF THE CITY OF LAKE ELSINORE, CALIFORNIA, PROHIBITING THE CONSTRUCTION OF NEW BUILDINGS, ADDITIONS OR ALTERATIONS, IN CERTAIN AREAS OF THE CITY AT OR BELOW CERTAIN ELEVATIONS.

The Mayor and the City Council of the City of Lake Elsinore, California, do ordain as follows:

Section 1: No person, firm or corporation shall construct any building upon any property within the City of Lake Elsinore with the foundation or basement lower than the elevation of 1270' mean sea level around the lake and along the channel to the spillway. Development on the Temescal Wash floodplain or within 5 vertical feet of the 100 year floodplain shall be subject to review on a case by case basis. No building permit shall be issued by the City which is in violation of the provisions of this ordinance and Ordinance No. 603.

Section 2: That any and all septic tanks, cesspools, leach lines, seepage pits shall not be constructed until written approval is obtained from the Department of Health of the County of Riverside.

Section 3: This ordinance shall remain in full force and effect until July 1, 1981, at which time this ordinance shall be of no effect except that the Ordinance No. 603 shall remain in full force and effect.

Section 4: The City Clerk shall cause this ordinance to be published as required by law.

Section 5: This ordinance is determined to be an urgency measure for the preservation of the Public Health, Safety and Welfare of the City of Lake Elsinore and will become effective immediately upon its adoption to reduce the possibility of injury and damage to persons or property due to possible flooding.

SELECTED REFERENCES ON FLOODING DUE TO FLUCTUATING LAKE LEVELS

Arnow, T. 1984, *Water Level and Water-Quality Changes in Great Salt Lake, Utah, 1847-1983.* Circular 913. Washington, D.C.: U.S. Geological Survey.

Carnelian-Marine Watershed District, 1982, *Overall Plan in Northeastern Washington County.* St. Paul, Minnesota: Carnelian-Marine Watershed District.

Cohen, P. and J. Stinchfield, 1984, *Shoreland Development Trends.* Report #4, Shoreland Update Program. St. Paul, Minnesota: Minnesota Dept. of Natural Resources.

Federal Emergency Management Agency, 1985, *Fluctuating Lakes: Case Studies and Mitigation Opportunities (draft),* Denver, Colorado: FEMA Region VIII.

International Great Lakes Levels Board, 1973, *Regulation of Great Lakes Water Levels, Report to the International Joint Commission.* Washington, D.C. and Ottawa, Ontario: International Joint Commission.

Joint Federal Regional Council, 1974, *A Strategy for Great Lakes Shoreland Damage Reduction.* Chicago: Great Lakes Basin Commission Task Force for Great Lakes Shorelands Damage Reduction.

Kay, P.A. and H.F. Diaz, 1985, *Problems of and Prospects for Predicting Great Salt Lake Levels.* Logan, Utah: University of Utah.

Minnesota Dept. of Natural Resources, 1980, Carnelian-Marine Watershed District miscellaneous files.

-------1982-84 Lake Pulaski correspondence files.

Novitzki, R.P. and R.W. Devane, 1978, *Wisconsin Lake Levels: Their Ups and Downs.* Madison, Wisconsin: U.S. Geological Survey and University of Wisconsin.

U.S. Army Corps of Engineers, 1983, *Devil's Lake Basin, North Dakota: Pre-Reconnaissance Evaluation Report.* St. Paul, Minnesota: St. Paul District, Corps of Engineers.

------, 1983, *Final Section 205 Detailed Project Report, Flood Control Project at Devil's Lake, North Dakota.* St. Paul, Minnesota: St. Paul District, Corps of Engineers.

------,1984, *Great Lakes Water Level Facts.* Detroit, Michigan: Detroit District, Corps of Engineers.

U.S. Geological Survey, 1976, *Hydrologic Relations Between Lakes and Aquifers in a Recharge Area Near Orlando, Florida.* Water Resources Investigation 76-65. Washington, D.C.: U.S. Government Printing Office.

------, 1979, *Analysis of Water-Level Fluctuations of Lakes Winona and Winnemissett--Two Landlocked Lakes in Karst Terrain in Volusia County, Florida.* Water Resources Investigations 79-55. Washington, D.C.: U.S. Government Printing Office.

Utah Dept. of Natural Resources and Energy, 1983, *Recommendations for a Great Salt Lake Contingency Plan for Influencing High and Low Levels of Great Salt Lake.* Salt Lake City, Utah: Division of State Lands and Forestry.

------,1984, *Great Salt Lake Summary of Technical Investigations for Water Level Control Alternatives.* Salt Lake City, Utah: Division of Water Resources.

Vaughan, R.D., 1984, *Utah Coping with Flooding: A Perspective on an Arid State.* Amherst, Massachusetts: University of Massachusetts Land and Water Policy Center.

Winter, T.G., 1983, *The Interaction of Lakes with Variably Saturated Porous Media.* Water Resources Research 19:1203-1218.

CHAPTER 9: GROUND FAILURE AREAS: SUBSIDENCE AND LIQUEFACTION

THE HAZARD

Subsidence and liquefaction are two types of ground failure which can lower the ground surface, causing or increasing flood damage in areas of high ground water, tides, storm surges or overbank stream flow. Mudflows and landslides are other types of ground failures which can cause flood damage. Subsidence is the most common type of failure and occurs in at least 38 states.

Both natural processes and human actions cause subsidence. Principal natural causes include solution (karst topography), consolidation of subsurface materials such as wetland soils and movements in the earth's crust. Principal human causes include mining, inadequate compaction of fill material during construction and withdrawal of oil or water from subsurface deposits. Human activities frequently accelerate natural processes.

Subsidence can increase flood damages in two ways. First, the land surface can be lowered so that it is more frequently or more deeply flooded. Second, subsidence can block or otherwise alter drainage patterns leading to deeper or unexpected flooding.

Causes of subsidence that have increased flooding problems include:

Withdrawal of Oil, Gas, Water. The withdrawal of oil, gas and water from below the earth's surface results in the collapse of the grain structure and compaction of subsurface materials causing the land surface to sink. The harbor at Long Beach, California has subsided as much as 27 feet due to oil and gas withdrawals. In the Houston-Galveston area of Texas, 2500 square miles have subsided one foot or more. Areas of Seabrook and Baytown, Texas, are now subject to flooding from daily tides.

Compaction of Organic Soils. Subsidence occurs in organic wetlands as the soils are compacted by fills and development and as ground water is withdrawn. The ground surface then settles, but not at an even rate. Development on coastal wetlands in coastal areas is most likely to experience subsidence.

Underground mining. Underground mining, both past and present, is the cause of subsidence in an estimated 220 counties in 42 states. Locally, this subsidence has worsened flooding and drainage problems in Pennsylvania and Illinois.

Karst Terrain. As ground water percolates through limestone, it dissolves the rock, forming cavities or caverns. Fluctuating ground water levels can cause these caverns and

Figure 9-1. These houses in Brownwood Subdivision are flooded by
daily tides because withdrawal of fluids has resulted in 2.5
meters of subsidence.   Source: R. Platt.

Figure 9-2. Organic soils like these are easily compressed, leading to subsidence.   Source: unknown.

Figure 9-3. Subsidence on organic soils has resulted in structural damage to this house in New Orleans.   Source: B. Cox.

overlying surface materials to collapse suddenly, forming sinkholes. The land surface can also sink slowly and irregularly, resulting in flooding.

Localized flooding occurs when natural drainage into and through caverns is blocked by silt, waste or rock dumped into caves and subsurface drainage channels. Voids in the limestone cannot always be detected. Cavern formation and collapse may be artificially accelerated by man's activities, for example withdrawal of ground water, which may have occurred far away from the site of the collapse.

Subsidence and flooding due to construction on organic soils is a widespread problem. There are an estimated 6.4 million acres of filled wetlands within metropolitan areas. The annual cost of subsidence damage in these areas has been estimated at $58 million and is expected to increase as the result of urban expansion onto lands normally considered unsuitable for development. In some cases, the cost of building streets to adequate standards in subsidence prone areas exceeds conventional construction costs by 80 percent.

Organic soil compaction has also been a problem in agricultural areas. Drainage of the Delta Islands of the Sacramento-San Joaquin Delta has resulted in lowering the surface of many of the islands to 10-15 feet below sea level. Subsidence can destroy the integrity of flood control levees and may necessitate continuous upgrading and maintenance of the levee system.

The risk of flood damage is higher in subsidence areas than in typical floodplain lands because the flood hazard is always increasing and the level of protection afforded by protection measures such as levees is always decreasing.

Liquefaction is another type of ground failure that contributes to flood problems. It is triggered by earthquakes. Liquefaction occurs when seismic shock waves pass through unconsolidated and saturated soil. Vibrations allow the soil grains to move freely and pack more closely together. Suddenly, instead of a soil structure with water in the pore spaces, there are groups of grains in a fluid matrix. The load of the overlying soil and buildings is transferred from the soil grains to the pore water. If the pressure on the water causes it to drain away, the overlying soil and structures will sink or tilt. If the water cannot drain away, the water pressure rises. When the water pressure equals the downward pressure of the overlying strata and structures, the saturated soil layer will become liquid and flow. On steep slopes (greater than 3%) where the saturated layer is at or near the surface, soil, vegetation and debris can flow rapidly downslope with the liquefied material. These flow failures can result in the movement of material for miles. On gentle slopes (0.3 to 3%) where the saturated layer is below the surface, huge blocks of soil can move 10 to 100 feet or more. Such failures are termed lateral spread.

Although strictly it is speaking not a flood problem, liquefaction can result in serious flooding of structures built on fill or saturated soils as in portions of San Francisco or Anchorage. In the 1964 Alaska earthquake in Prince William Sound, 60% of the $500 million in damages was due to ground failure.

EXISTING MITIGATION EFFORTS

Flood-related subsidence and liquefaction areas have not been extensively mapped or regulated, nor are ground failure conditions reflected in flood mapping for insurance and other management purposes. The failure to integrate mapping, regulation and other management of these natural hazards is a reflection of the fragmentation of responsibilities for these activities at all levels of government. Better integration can be expected in the future as a result of the current focus on more comprehensive approaches to emergency management.

Subsidence

Some of the earliest efforts to prevent subsidence began in California. Ground water overdraft in the Santa Clara Valley from 1920 to the late 1960's resulted in 13 feet of subsidence. By 1969, subsidence had essentially stopped due to recharge of ground water and importation of surface water through the State Water Project.

Frequently, the remedy for the subsidence problem requires a regional rather than a site specific approach. The Harris-Galveston Subsidence District and the Active Ground Water Management Areas in Arizona are examples of the kinds of institutional arrangements that have been established to solve regional problems. In both cases, the purpose is to reduce subsidence by regulating ground water overdraft. The enabling legislation of the Harris Galveston Subsidence District is summarized and presented in Appendix 9-A; excerpts from the proposed district plan are presented in Appendix 9-B.

One of the problems in mitigating karst and/or sinkhole hazards has been the lack of ability to find them in the subsurface before they result in land surface collapse. Improved detection techniques as well as better management of surface water drainage are integral parts of sinkhole hazard mitigation. The stormwater management program in Bowling Green, Warren County, Kentucky addresses both flooding and land use in sinkhole areas.

Illinois and Pennsylvania have adopted regulatory programs to reduce subsidence due to the extractions of minerals. Several techniques are employed to reduce the subsidence threat including leaving rock pillars and filling cavities with compacted mine waste. Impacts of these and other alternatives on the hydrology for the area have to be carefully considered because of the potential for impacts on quantity and quality of flow.

Liquefaction

Considerable progress has been made in determining where liquefaction is likely to occur. The characteristics of the liquefaction prone area are:

1. geologically young, unconsolidated sands and silts.

2. presence of the water table within 50 feet of the land surface.

Progress has also been made in determining the frequency of "shaking" which produces liquefaction areas. For example, in the San Fernando Valley in California, data suggest that such levels of shaking occur approximately once every 45 years.

The relationship between liquefaction and flooding is that most liquefaction prone areas are in the floodplains of active seismic areas. In the Los Angeles area, the areas most prone to liquefaction include the floodplains of the Los Angeles, Santa Anna and San Gabriel Rivers and flood control basins. In the New Madrid seismic zone of the Central Mississippi Valley, liquefaction can occur as far as 150 kilometers away from the epicenter of a major earthquake. Again, the most liquefaction prone areas are the floodplains and, in this case, hundreds of miles of levees could be affected.

OPTIONS FOR COMMUNITY ACTION

Policy and Program Elements

A community policy and program to address subsidence and liquefaction problems should include the following elements:

1. A statement by the legislative body that subsidence and liquefaction are problems which are to be reflected in ongoing floodplain management;

2. Mapping of subsidence and liquefaction areas with, if possible, determination of the rates of subsidence and frequency of liquefaction-producing events.

3. Adoption of development controls for subsidence and liquefaction areas. Man-made causes of subsidence such as ground water extraction should be

Table 9-1: Data Needs and Management Options for Subsidence: Source: HRB-Singer, Inc., from a report prepared for U.S. HUD, 1977.

SUBSIDENCE CONDITION	GEOLOGIC AND PEDOLOGIC PARAMETERS CONSIDERED	REQUIRED TEST DATA	DETECTION AND PREDICTION TECHNIQUES USED	SITE ENGINEERING AND FOUNDATION ALTERNATIVES	
				LOCAL	AREAL
Underground mining (bituminous coal)	Seam thickness Thickness of overburden Lithology of overburden, mine roof, mine floor Span (of void) Minimum pillar diameter Percentage extraction Time since mining Remnant pillar pattern Water table level Fracturing Angle of draw (limit angle) Angle of break	Mining history of area (PA) Subsurface investigation for multifamily housing (PA)	Mining history from maps, records Borings Borehole camera	Grade beams Caissons Grout columns Structural slabs or rafts	Fly ash injection Flushing Daylighting

Drained organic wetlands	Soil composition
	Soil compaction
	Soil shrinkage
	Soil decomposition
	Water table levels
	Buried canals
	Drainage
	Soil thickness
		MPS's require borings and evaluations of engineered foundation for subdivisions and single family dwellings; borings, soils tests, and foundations reports for multifamily construction (LA)	Borings
			
			Maps:
			  Geologic
			  Pedologic
			  Vegetation
				Piles (timber)
				
				Raymond piles (high rises)
				Kelley slab
				Conventional slab, Types 1, 2, and 3
				Mud jacking
					Surcharging
					Maintaining water level
					Removing organic soil

Sinkhole formation	Lithology Water table fluctuation Pumping rates and volumes Discharge of water into limestone Overburden Fracture patterns	Soils and boring data for multifamily units (PA) Minimum 100-foot borings for high rises (FA)	Borings Seismic tests Gravity metering Aerial photography Topographic maps Resistivity (PA) Air rotary drilling (PA)	Slab on grade Piles Grouting Spread footings Raft foundation Filling shallow cavities Slabbing over deep cavities BRAB Slab (PA)	Avoiding sinkhole areas Maintaining water table levels

regulated. Structures should be constructed at elevations reflecting anticipated subsidence rates.

Since subsidence and liquefaction are often regional problems, they must be addressed at several levels: by individual property owners, by subdividers or developments
and by groups of municipalities. Coordination of these efforts is essential. Municipalities
must direct new development toward more stable areas and establish building standards.
Developers have the responsibility to use adequate design and construction techniques.

Mapping

Different procedures are needed for mapping subsidence or liquefaction areas.

Subsidence

Data needs and management options for subsidence areas are given in Table 9-1.

Subsidence due to fluid withdrawal. Areas subject to subsidence due to fluid withdrawal can often be identified only through time-series topographic information indicating actual lowering of the ground surface. Once identified, rates can be estimated. Analysis of an aquifer's water budget by computer modeling can also be used to suggest likely
areas of subsidence and, in some cases, the rates of subsidence.

A general idea of the potential for subsidence due to ground water withdrawal can
be obtained by comparing withdrawal with recharge on a regional basis. The U.S. Geological Survey publishes hydrologic atlases for many areas of the country that indicate
aquifer recharge rates.

More sophisticated computerized models have been developed to evaluate ground
water recharge and withdrawal and express the results in terms of projected subsidence. A
two model system developed by the U.S. Geological Survey has been applied to the Houston-Galveston area. The first model uses data on ground water pumpage to predict
changes in the ground water level. Long-term reduction of ground water changes in levels
is likely to result in subsidence. A second model relates changes in the water table level to
changes in the land surface elevation.

Subsidence on organic (wetland) soils. Organic wetland soils can be identified with
soil maps and onsite inspections. Generally, the entire area underlain by organic soil
should be designated a subsidence risk area. If water table records are available, areas of
naturally dropping water table levels are particularly high risk.

Subsidence on Karst Terrain. Karst areas are underlain by limestone and other water soluble minerals that can be identified on geologic maps prepared by the U.S. or State

Geological Surveys. However, the presence of these deposits does not necessarily mean that karst conditions exist. Even where geologic maps show karst areas, predicting specific subsidence and flooding in karst is difficult without field studies including soil boring and dye tests.

Where development is located in gradual sinkholes (forming depressions without outlets) and the flood threat is due to surface drainage into the sinkholes, standard runoff models can be used to predict flood levels with a few modifications. Bowling Green, Kentucky has made the following assumptions with the use of such models:

1. The city assumes no outflow since sinkholes may be filled, blocked or flooded beyond drainage capacity.

2. The city uses a 24-hour rainfall event. While hourly intensities are used in non-karst areas, the interval is longer for sinkholes since they drain much more slowly than stream channels.

3. The city assumes runoff levels with maximum urbanization.

4. The city adds at least one foot of freeboard above the 100-year elevation contour.

Bowling Green requires developers to map flood depths in sinkhole basins since there are many, small (1-1/2 acre) sinkhole drainage basins in the area.

The Florida Bureau of Geology in cooperation with the Florida Sinkhole Research Institute is currently mapping areas of the state drained by sinkholes. They are developing methods to characterize drainage into and through sinkholes based on vegetation and soil factors that affect infiltration of water.

Liquefaction

The U.S. Geological Survey and state geological surveys have been particularly active in mapping liquefaction-prone areas. The urban areas of San Diego, Los Angeles, San Francisco, Salt Lake City, Seattle, Albuquerque, Anchorage and Reno are currently being studied. Figure 9-4 depicts the regulated liquefaction areas near San Francisco Bay in Redwood City, California. These areas were mapped by the USGS and are regulated by the city. FEMA is continuing evaluations of the impacts of a severe earthquake in the active seismic areas of the west and the New Madrid Seismic Zone. Mapping of liquefaction zones is one of the products of these studies.

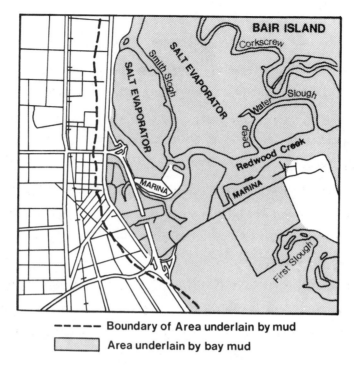

Figure 9-4. Part of a map showing the area of Redwood City, CA underlain by bay mud. The map is attached to the building code which requires supplemental structural design and construction standards for all new development.   Source: U.S.G.S.

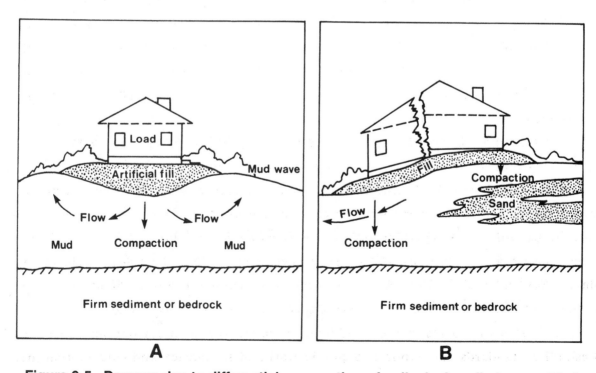

Figure 9-5. Damage due to differential compaction of soils. In A, soils have settled homogeneously. In B., the presence of the sand body results in differential settling with subsequent structural damage to the house. Source: U.S.G.S.

Regulation

The type of regulation needed to reduce damage in subsidence and liquefaction areas depend on the cause and severity of the subsidence or liquefaction (see Table 2 for summary of regulatory options). There are two basic approaches to subsidence-related flood damages:

1. Regulate the cause of the subsidence.

2. Regulate land use or construction practices in subsidence areas.

The first approach is not generally applicable to liquefaction (which is due to natural causes); the second approach is appropriate for both subsidence and liquefaction.

Regulations for subsidence and liquefaction areas may take several forms:

Building codes can be used to establish special foundation requirements for structures on organic soils or in liquefaction areas. See Appendix 9-C for building code provisions adopted by Jefferson Parish, Louisiana to reduce damage to development on organic soils.

There are two design approaches for liquefaction areas:

1. Determine the depths to which liquefaction may occur through soil testing and surveys, then require piles to be placed to the bottom.

2. Determine the area subject to liquefaction, then "load" it prior to development so that the pore water is forced out and soil density is increased.

Where subsidence or liquefaction potential exists but detailed studies are lacking, require developers to conduct geologic and engineering studies to determine actual risks and design accordingly. This type of ordinance would identify the geographic areas with potential risk, establish study requirements, and specify qualifications for study contractors.

Zoning and building codes can be used to require additional freeboard in floodplain regulations to reflect subsidence. Such regulations can also be used to reduce damage in karst terrain. For example, the Bowling Green, Warren County, Kentucky stormwater management program addresses both the cause of flooding and land uses. Filling of sinkholes which will block drainage and cause flooding is prohibited. The floodplain ordinance also requires mapping and restricts development below the 100-year flood elevation in sinkhole basins. The subdivision ordinance requires drainage plans for all new development and on-site detention to prevent increase in stormwater runoff.

Infrastructure plans, zoning, subdivision controls or other regulations can be used to establish standards for public and public works in subsidence and liquefaction areas.

Unit construction can be required for roads, walks and other paved surfaces, expansion loops can be required for utility pipes and lines.

Special codes can be used to regulate ground water withdrawals, the removal of gas and oil or the mining of minerals. See Appendix 9-A for excerpts from the enabling statute and regulations from the Houston-Galveston Coastal Subsidence District.

Table 9-2 summarizes the options for various types of subsidence.

Nonregulatory Actions.

Nonregulatory actions for reducing damage include:

Construction of Retention Basins and Drainage Systems

A community can construct retention basins and drainage systems for karst terrain to reduce runoff into depressions where existing development is located.

Relocation

In some places, for example the Brownwood subdivision in Baytown, Texas, where subsidence has lowered the ground surface to below sea level, relocation is the only practical alternative. More than 200 houses have been purchased in this subdivision and relocated or demolished with funds from FEMA's Section 1362 program and local funding sources.

Control of Surface Water Elevations in Organic Soil Areas

Surface water elevations should be carefully controlled for large lowlying areas of organic soil that must be saturated to remain stable.

In lowland areas of organic soils which are drained by canals, drainage and subsidence go hand-in-hand. Canals are dug deeper in the attempt to drain the lowest lands. Deep canals drain water from the surface water table and cause subsidence. The land owners, again subject to flooding, will want still deeper canals, and the cycle begins anew.

Areawide monitoring of drainage canal levels and ground water table levels coupled with subsidence records and regional hydrologic data can be used to determine optimum water levels in the canals and ground water. Expert hydrologic advice is needed.

Table 9-2: Regulatory Options for Subsidence-Related Flooding

	Regulate Cause	Regulate Land-Use and Construction
Organic Soils	Not generally applicable.	Prohibit development in severe subsidence prone areas. Adopt construction codes for buildings, walks and drives and utilities. Include freeboard requirement based on subsidence potential. Adopt disclosure requirement for real estate.
Karst Terrain	Prohibit ground water withdrawals which may result in subsidence of land above. Prevent filling or other blockages to drainage in sinkholes where such blockages may cause flooding.	Prohibit development in high risk areas. Adopt disclosure requirement for real estate transactions. Adopt storm water management regulations where flooding may be due to drainage into sinkholes.
Fluid Withdrawal	Control ground water or oil and gas withdrawals. Adopt reinjection requirements for oil and gas fields.	Prohibit construction in severely subsiding areas. Require freeboard in floodplain regulations to reflect subsidence rates. Adopt disclosure requirements for real estate transactions.
Abandoned Mines	Require special bracing or mining to avoid possible subsidence reclamation of mined areas.	Prohibit development in high risk areas. Require purchase of surface easement or development rights for new mining ventures. Adopt disclosure requirements for real estate transactions.

Public Awareness of Subsidence

Subsidence is often a continuing and not obvious process. Individuals who own property in a subsiding area face an ongoing repair job. Newcomers to an area may not consider subsidence when selecting property or constructing a building. If they do, they may value practical advice on available remedial measures and alternatives. Guidance through brochures or slide programs is valuable. Civic groups could be encouraged and assisted to act as a clearinghouse for information.

Appendix 9-A: Outline and Excerpts from an Act of the Texas Legislature.

HOUSE BILL NO. 552,

relating to the creation, establishment, administration, powers, duties, functions, and financing of the Harris-Galveston Coastal Subsidence District.

Sec. 1. PURPOSE AND INTENT

    (a)   The purpose of this Act is to provide for the regulation of the withdrawal of ground water within the boundaries of the district for the purpose of ending subsidence which contributes to or precipitates flooding, inundation. or overflow of any area within the district including without limitation rising waters resulting from storms or hurricanes.

Sec. 2. DEFINITIONS. In this Act:

    (a)   "Subsidence" means the lowering in elevation of the surface of land by the withdrawal of ground water.

Sec. 3. CREATION

Sec. 4. BOUNDARIES.

    (a)   The district shall include all of the area located within the boundaries of Harris County and Galveston County.

Sec. 5. BOARD OF DIRECTORS.

    (a)   The district shall be governed by a board of directors composed of 15 members.

Sec. 6. POWERS AND DUTIES IN GENERAL.

The board shall administer the provisions of this Act...Withdrawals of ground water covered by the Provisions of this Act are subject to reasonable rules, regulations, and orders adopted by the board, taking into account all factors including availability of surface water, economic impact upon persons and the community, degree and effect of subsidence upon the surface of land, and differing topographical and geophysical characteristics of land areas within the district.

Sec. 7. GENERAL MANAGER.

Sec. 8. EMPLOYEES.

Sec. 9. DISTRICT OFFICE

Sec. 10. MINUTES AND RECORDS OF THE DISTRICT.

Sec. 11. SUITS

Sec. 12. SEAL

Sec. 13. RULES AND REGULATIONS.

(a) After notice and hearing under Section 14 of this Act, the board shall adopt and enforce rules and regulations that are designed to expeditiously and effectively effectuate the provisions of this Act and accomplish its purposes, including rules governing Procedure before the board.

Sec. 14. HEARINGS.

Sec. 15. COMPELLING TESTIMONY, SWEARING WITNESSES, AND SUBPOENAS.

Sec. 16. DISTRICT PLAN

(a) Under Section 14 of this Act, the board shall formulate a plan to control and prevent subsidence within the district. The plan shall accomplish this purpose by the reduction of ground water withdrawals to amounts which will restore and maintain sufficient artesian pressure to control and prevent subsidence....

Sec. 17. PLANNING PROCEDURES.

Sec. 18. TEMPORARY REGULATION.

Sec. 19. PERMIT REQUIREMENT.

Sec. 20. TERM OF PERMIT

Sec. 21. RENEWAL OF PERMIT.

Sec. 22. APPLICATION FOR PERMIT.

Sec. 23. NOTICE AND HEARING ON PERMIT

Sec. 24. DECISION AND ISSUANCE OF PERMIT.

(b) In deciding whether or not to issue a permit and in setting the terms of the Permit, the board shall consider, along with the purpose of this Act and all other relevant factors:

(1) the district plan;

(2) the quality, quantity, and availability of surface water at prices competitive with those charged by suppliers of surface water within the district;

(3)   the economic impact on the applicant from grant or denial of the permit, or the terms prescribed by a permit, in relation to the effect on subsidence that would result.

(c)   The board shall grant a permit to an applicant whenever it is found upon presentation of adequate proof that there is no other adequate and available substitute or supplemental source of surface waters at prices competitive with those charged by suppliers of surface water within the district and that compliance with any provision of this Act, or any rule or regulation of the district, will result in an arbitrary taking of Property or in the practical closing and elimination of any lawful business. occupation, or activity, in either case without sufficient corresponding benefit or advantage to the people.

(d)   If the board decides to issue the permit, the permit shall be issued to the applicant stating the terms prescribed by the board.

(e)   The permit shall include the following:

     (1)   the name and address of the person to whom the permit is issued;

     (2)   the location of the well;

     (3)   the date the permit is to expire;....

Sec. 25. PERMIT NOT TRANSFERABLE.

Sec. 26. ANNUAL REPORTS.

Sec. 27. BOARD INVESTIGATIONS.

Sec. 28. ANNUAL GROUND WATER WITHDRAWAL DETERMINATION.

Sec. 29. REGULATION OF SPACING AND PRODUCTION.

(a)   In order to minimize as far as practicable the drawdown of the water table and reduction of artesian pressure and to control and prevent subsidence, the board may provide for the spacing of wells and regulate the production of ground water from wells, taking into consideration, among other relevant factors, the economic impact on well-owners and the resulting effect on subsidence.

Sec. 30. REQUIRING WATER-METERING DEVICES.

Sec. 31. ACCESS TO PROPERTY.

Sec. 32. MONITORING AND SUPERVISIONS OF DISTRICT.

Sec. 33. RESEARCH AND STUDIES.

Appendix 9-B. Excerpts of the Harris-Galveston Coastal Subsidence District Proposed District Plan, July 16, 1985.

I. Purpose and Intent:

It is the purpose and intent of this Plan to establish policy in the areas of technical research and studies, water conservation, public information, regulation, permits and enforcement and equity and discretion; and to set forth a Regulatory Action Plan which divides the district into regulatory areas and establishes regulatory objectives for each area.

II. Definitions: section omitted

III. Background

The Harris-Galveston Coastal Subsidence District was created...to regulate the withdrawal of groundwater within Harris and Galveston Counties. The District was created "...for the purpose of ending subsidence which contributes to or precipitates flooding, inundation, or overflow of any area within the district, including without limitation rising waters resulting from storms or hurricanes."

In 1976, the District adopted a District Plan, written as an interim plan designed to have an immediate impact on the subsidence problem in the area most vulnerable to the damaging effects of subsidence. The 1976 Plan recognized its technical deficiencies and provided that a new plan would be adopted when a broader technical basis for regulation was established.

In adopting the 1976 Plan, the District focused on the southeastern part of Harris County and all of Galveston County and was primarily concerned with the elimination of subsidence and the reduction of potential damage caused by flooding in that area. Much progress in controlling subsidence in that area, known as the ACE, has been made. Around the Houston Ship Channel,, for example, less than one-tenth of one foot of subsidence has been recorded in the last eight years. No subsidence was recorded in 1984. Water-level increases in the aquifer system in amounts up to 150 feet have been measured. Two significant factors have contributed immensely to successful results in the ACE: (1) the availability of surface water and (2) the conservation of water by industry. The availability of surface water in this area alone has been of tremendous benefit in curbing subsidence. Surface-water supplies, however, are not available in other areas currently experiencing rapid rates of subsidence. Without surface-water supplies, a dramatic reduction in groundwater pumping, and consequently in subsidence rates, cannot be expected. Construction of surface-water treatment facilities and transmission lines is absolutely essential for controlling subsidence.

During the time that the District focused on the ACE, extensive growth was experienced in western Harris County. As a result, groundwater withdrawal has increased dramatically and subsidence has become an issue for local governments and concerned citizens. Although inland areas are not at risk from storm surge and coastal flooding, groundwater withdrawal in those areas affects subsidence not only in the inland areas but also in the coastal areas. While the emphasis of the first District Plan was to control subsidence in the ACE, the intent of this Plan is to extend the focus to inland areas as well.

IV. Policy

This portion of the Plan establishes policy...regarding technical research and studies, water conservation, public information, regulation, permits and enforcement and equity and discretion. These policies are designed to support the regulation of groundwater withdrawal to control subsidence on a regional basis. Because subsidence is a region-wide problem requiring solutions achieved through concerted efforts, the District will work with other entities in the region to implement this Plan.

A. Technical Research and Studies.

...the District has completed several technical projects that provide a more sophisticated basis for regulatory policy. They include...:

1. A well data base...to maintain accurate and up-to-date information on well location, ownership, construction, pumpage and permit status...

2. The maintenance and operation of thirteen subsidence monitors at eleven locations...Each monitor provides a continuous record of elevation change and represents the only subsidence information available between releveling surveys. ...The potentiometric surface of each aquifer is measured annually and analyzed with respect to the previous year's pumpage.

3. A comprehensive, regional releveling completed in 1978 and limited releveling surveys in 1976 and 1983. The relevelings, while periodic, provide elevation data on a broad geographical basis.

4. A two-phase, comprehensive water management study completed in 1982. This study developed and refined "state-of-the-art" computer models to give the District the ability to evaluate the effects of varying pumpage patterns over time to predict the resulting subsidence. The capability of the computer modeling system has been used to forecast rates and amounts of subsidence in different locations and to project surface-water use necessary to meet the objectives and requirements of this Plan.

...Although the technical accomplishments...have contributed significantly to the ability to evaluate and control subsidence, there are at least four areas that require immediate attention...:

1. An engineering study, or studies, to determine and evaluate the effects of inland subsidence on flooding.

2. Additional subsidence monitors in areas that are not adequately covered by existing monitors.

3. A regional releveling in 1986 and every six to ten years thereafter.

4. The continued study of the effect of subsidence on surface drainage in the Houston area by evaluating changes in the topography of well fields.

B. Water Conservation

The District will support water conservation efforts to help control subsidence and to optimize the use of a valuable natural resource. Conservation measures may be required as a condition on certain well permits to reduce groundwater pumpage...

C. Public Information

The District believes that dissemination of information is vital in controlling subsidence and recognizes the value of the support of an informed public...

D. Regulation

...The District will determine the effect of subsidence on flooding in inland areas...Until this determination is made, the District will regulate groundwater withdrawal to control subsidence in those inland areas.

The number of regulatory areas and the boundaries of each may change as conditions change. Relevant factors to be considered in establishing or changing area boundaries include changes in pumpage, changes in groundwater levels, relationship of subsidence to flooding and the availability of surface water...

E. Permits and Enforcement

The District may deny permits or limit groundwater withdrawal...the District will weigh the public benefit against individual hardship....In carrying out its purpose, the District is empowered to require the reduction of groundwater withdrawal to amounts that will restore and maintain sufficient artesian pressure to control and prevent subsidence....

F. Equity and Discretion

The District recognizes that the burden of controlling subsidence should be borne by all users of groundwater. Groundwater withdrawal by any person must be regulated when it works in concert with other groundwater withdrawal to produce subsidence, even though that person's groundwater withdrawal of itself would be incapable of producing subsidence...

V. Regulatory Action Plan

This portion of the Plan...translates the legislative mandate of the District and the policy of this Plan into specific objectives and requirements. It divides the District into eight areas and establishes requirements for each area. For purposes of information, it also estimates future water requirements and projects subsidence.

A. Regulatory Objectives

The legislative mandate to end "subsidence which contributes to or precipitates flooding, inundation or overflow of any area within the district..."

B. Division of the District into Areas

For the purpose of regulation, the District is divided into eight areas which are based on a commonality of regulatory interests and goals as well as economic and technical considerations. These areas are interrelated...

C. Regulatory Requirements

1. Area One

a. Through 1989, as a general rule, increases in groundwater withdrawal will not be permitted.

b. Beginning in 1990, groundwater withdrawal must be reduced so that no more than 10% of the total water use is from ground water.

2. Area Two

a. Through 1989, as a general rule, increases in groundwater withdrawal may be permitted so long as surface-water use is not reduced.

b. In 1990 groundwater withdrawal must be reduced so that no more than 20% of the total water use is from groundwater.

c. Thereafter through 1998, increases in groundwater withdrawal may be permitted so long as surface-water use is not decreased. Then in 1999, groundwater withdrawal again must be reduced so that no more than 20% of the total water use is from groundwater.

d. Thereafter through 2006, increases in groundwater withdrawal may be permitted so long as surface-water use is not decreased. Then in 2007, groundwater withdrawal again must be reduced so that no more than 20% of total water use is from groundwater.

e. Thereafter through 2-14 years, increases in groundwater withdrawal may be permitted so long as surface-water use is not decreased. Then in 2015, groundwater withdrawal again must be reduced so that no more than 20% of the total water use is from groundwater.

f. Thereafter through 2020, increases in groundwater withdrawal may be permitted so long as surface-water use is not decreased.

D. Estimated Water Requirements and Projected Subsidence

The District has projected total water demand and established regulatory requirements that permit limited amounts of groundwater to be withdrawn...It is necessary that surface water supply the difference between groundwater and total demand. If the surface-water supply is inadequate, then total water demand must decrease. The options available to reduce total water demand are limiting growth and implementing mandatory water conservation programs.

In projecting total water demand, the District has modified prior growth projections using actual developments of the past few years. As new official growth projections become available, regulatory requirements may be changed.

In showing the amounts of groundwater that will be permitted, the District generally will allow, in areas other than the coastal area, growth on groundwater between the years in which additional surface water realistically can be introduced given the time and cost necessary to construct surface-water treatment facilities and transmission systems.

Using its computer modeling system, the District predicts that implementation of this Plan may result in additional subsidence....This subsidence is the amount expected to occur given the realistic capability of other entities to develop surface-water supplies and construct treatment and transmission systems....

Appendix 9-C Excerpts of Building Code and Related Regulations of the Parish of Jefferson, Louisiana.

Part X Detailed Regulations

Chapter 28 - Excavation, Footings and Foundations

Article 2801. **Subsoil Investigation**

Where the soil bearing capacity for spread foundations or the pile load capacity is not known, undisturbed soil borings shall be made under the direction of the Louisiana Registered Civil Engineer or Louisiana Registered Architect, experienced in soil mechanics. Number and depth of borings shall be influenced by the importance, type, size, and location of the structure...An engineering analysis establishing soil bearing capacity, pile load capacity, depth of foundation, expected settlement, depth of the ground water table, and the like, as applicable, shall be made....This data required shall be obtained from a minimum of one soil boring for structures under three stories and not over 10,000 square feet ground floor area, two soil borings for other structures less than 15,000 square feet of ground floor area and one additional boring for each 15,000 square feet of ground floor area.

ARTICLE 2802. **Excavations.**

(a)   Design. All excavations for structures covered by this code shall be designed in accordance with established engineering principles. The design shall utilize soil characteristics determined by borings and laboratory tests...

ARTICLE 2803. **Foundations.**

Foundations shall be built upon naturally solid ground or upon properly compacted fill material, or shall be built with pilings. Foundations shall be constructed of masonry, plain concrete, reinforced concrete, or of piling materials described in this chapter....

ARTICLE 2804. **Spread Foundations.**

(a)   Design. Footings are to be so designed that the allowable bearing capacity of the soil shall not be exceeded.

(b)   Soil Bearing Capacity.

   1.   The Director may accept the soil bearing capacity established by the engineering analysis.. as meeting minimum requirements.

   2.   In addition to the engineering analysis, or in lieu thereof, the Director may require load bearing tests of the soil...to determine the allowable bearing capacity of the soil. The method of testing shall be in accordance with ASTM D1194 "Standard Methods of Testing the Bearing Capacity of Soil for Static Load on Spread Footings." On all tests, the location of the ground water table shall be noted. The allowable soil bearing shall be one-half the load at the yield point. However, settlement of the test plate at allowable load shall not exceed one-quarter of the gross settlement.

3.   The Director may accept other adequate proof as to the soil bearing capacity at a particular location.

ARTICLE 2805. **Pile Foundations.**

(a)   Design.

1.   Piles shall be designed to include all weights and forces applied to their butts including the weight of mats or caps and the weight of earth or fill on top of the mats or caps considering the effect of buoyance; the weight of the piles shall be given due consideration in the foundation design. In cases where piles are loaded eccentrically, due provisions shall be made for such eccentricities....

4.   Where the soil boring records of site conditions indicate possible deleterious action on pile materials because of soil constituents, changing water levels, electrolysis, corrosion, or other factors, such materials shall be adequately protected. The effectiveness of such methods or processes for the particular purpose shall have been thoroughly established by satisfactory service records or other evidence which demonstrated the effectiveness of such protective measures. Cut-off of untreated wood piles shall not be higher than the lowest ground water level anticipated for the life of the building as determined by an engineering investigation or established data, but in no case shall the cut-off be less than 7 feet below natural ground surface. Structural steel piles driven below the permanent water table and also into natural soil need not be protected against electrolysis and/or corrosion....

ARTICLE 2813. **Residential and Small Foundations.**

(a)   General. This section of the code covers the following: I - Occupancy (Residence 1-4 units), J - Occupancy (Accessory Building not to exceed 1,000 square feet), and all other structures, including small commercial which do not exceed 5,000 square feet in gross floor area and do not exceed 35 feet in height. This section of the building Code addresses the challenge of designing foundations compatable with our unique soils. Among the problems associated with the urban devedlopment of our soils are: Initial and continued soil subsidence, high shrink-swell potential of firm clays, severe wetness, low bearing strength, the necessity of having to add fill material and continuous lowering of the water table. Because of these potential problems, design of foundations should be based on an onsite subsoil investigation whenever possible, as per Article 2801 of the Code....

(b)   Pile Foundations. All areas having soils which contain one or more of the above mentioned limitations that may occur as a result of man or nature should have a properly designed pile supported foundation. The unincorporated areas of Jefferson Parish, as outlined on the U.S. Soil Conservation Survey East Bank of Jefferson Parish Soil Map, September, 1977, and on the U.S. Soil Conservation Survey West Bank of Jefferson Parish Soil Map, September, 1978, delineate areas where pile foundations are required and where pile foundations are not required, but recommended. All areas not covered by the maps shall require a subsoil investigation as per Article 2801 of the Code.

1.   Residential piles shall comply with all applicable requirements of this chapter as provided in this article. Piles shall be properly held in line or adequately tied together at their butt end by means of continuous reinforced concrete or equivalent construction. Pile butts shall be protected by a minimum of 3 inches of concrete around their perimeter. All piles for a building or a structure should extend to the same depth unless adequate provisions for a differential settlement within the building or structure have been made. The Director shall be notified by the party installing the piles at least 24 hours in advance of any pile driving....

2.   When pile foundations are required, maximum design load capacities have been established for various types and embedments of piles. These values are tabulated for each area which requires pile foundations and are shown on the U.S. Soil Conservation Survey Maps of the East Bank of Jefferson Parish... and the West Bank of Jefferson Parish...In soil type (13) Sharkey Clay, a special foundation may be used in lieu of a pile supported foundation, provided the foundation design is prepared by or under the direct supervision of a Louisiana Registered Civil Engineer or Louisiana Registered Architect experienced in soil mechanics; such drawings and specifications shall be designated per lot and square and be imprinted with this seal, and these plans shall be approved by the Department of Inspection & Code Enforcement, prior to issuance of the building permit....

The Standards of the Code regarding the need for a pile foundation or the maximum design load capacity for the particular type of pile may be superseded by a subsoil investigation which is performed in accordance with Article 2801 or a pile load test which is performed in accordance with Article 2805 provided the subsoil investigation or pile load test is located within a 150 foot radius of the proposed foundation for a single boring or pile test...

4.(c) Site Filling. The use of the pile capacities contained in this article shall be limited only to situations in which downdrag is not a significant factor.

Design use of these capacities shall be limited to areas where fill is less than 2 feet in thickness unless the area is brought to grade for an adequate preload period prior to driving piles. Recommended preload periods are as follows:

Fill Thickness	Preload
2 to 3 feet	2 to 3 months
3 to 4 feet	3 to 6 months
4 to 5 feet	6 to 9 months

Specific considerations must be made for construction over filled canals, ditches, or unusual local conditions. The thickness of the fill shall be measured from the natural ground surface. This shall be determined with a minimum of 5 elevations taken on each corner of the structure and in the middle of the structure.

SELECTED REFERENCES ON FLOODING DUE TO GROUND FAILURE

Allen, A.S., 1969, *Geological Settings in Subsidence*. In Varnes, D.J. and S. Kiersch, eds. Review in Engineering Geology 2: 305-342. Boulder, Colorado: Geological Society of America.

Beck, B.F., 1985, *Sinkholes: Their Geology, Engineering and Environmental Impact*. Proceedings of First Multidisciplinary Conference on Sinkholes.

Canderib, Fleissig and Associates, 1973, *Demonstration of a Technique for Limiting the Subsidence of Land over Abandoned Mines, Final Report, Rock Springs, Wyoming*. Washington, D.C.: U.S. Dept. of Housing and Urban Development.

Federal Emergency Management Agency, 1979, *A Preliminary Study of Subsidence Mitigation Policies and Technologies*. Incomplete draft. Washington, D.C.: FEMA.

------, 1983, *The National Earthquake Hazard Reduction Program*: A Report to the Congress, Detailed Program Information. Fiscal Year 1982. Washington, D.C.: FEMA.

Fowler, L.C., 1981, *Economic Consequences of Land Surface Subsidence, Journal of the Irrigation and Drainage Division*, Proceedings, ASCE 107 (1R2): 151-159.

Gabrysch, R.K. and C.W. Bonnet, 1974, *Land-surface Subsidence in the Areas of Burnett, Scott and Crystal Bays near Baytown, Texas*. Water Resources Investigation 21-24. Washington, D.C.: U.S. Geological Survey.

------,1975, Land-surface *Subsidence in the Houston-Galveston Region, Texas*. Report 188. Austin, Texas: Texas Water Development Board and U.S. Geological Survey.

Gary, M., R. McAfee, J. Wolf and C.L. Wolf, eds, 1977, *Glossary of Geology*. Washington, D.C.: American Geological Institute.

General Analytics, Inc. 1974, *State of the Art of Subsidence Control and Abandoned Mines*. Report by the Comptroller General. Washington, D.C.: U.S. Government Printing Office.

Helm, D.C., 1982, *Conceptual Aspects of Subsidence due to Fluid Withdrawal*. In Narasimiham, T.N., Ed. Recent Trends in Hydrology. Special Paper 189. Boulder, Colorado: Geological Society of America.

Holzer, T.L., 1977, *Ground Failure in Areas of Subsidence due to Ground Water Decline in the U.S. Proceedings, International Symposium on Land Subsidence*. Publication 121. Anaheim, California: International Association of Hydrological Services.

------, 1984, *Man-Induced Land Subsidence*. Boulder, Colorado: Geological Society of America.

Hooper, M.G., S.T. Algermissen and E.E. Dobrovolny, 1983, *Estimation of Earthquake Effects Associated with a Great Earthquake in the New Madrid Seismic Zone.* CUSEPP Report No. 82-3. U.S. Geological Survey Open File Report 83-179. Washington, D.C.: USGS.

Johnson, C., 1976, *The Undermining of Butte, Montana.* The Washington Post, November 22.

Kopper, W. and D. Finlayson, 1981, *Legal Aspects of Subsidence Due to Well Pumping.* Journal of the Irrigation and Drainage Division, Proceedings, ASCE 107 (1R2): 137-149.

Lee, S. and D.R. Nichols, 1981, Subsidence. In: Hays, W.W., ed. *Facing Geologic and Hydrological Hazards, Earth-Science Considerations.* Professional Paper 1240-B. Washington, D.C.: U.S. Geological Survey.

Lofgren, B.E., 1969, *Land Subsidence due to Application of Waters.* In Varnes, D.J. and G. Kierzch, eds. Reviews in Engineering Geology 2. Boulder, Colorado: Geological Society of America.

Morton, D.R., 1979, *A Selected Bibliography of Recent Subsidence Studies*, University of Colorado, Natural Hazards Research and Applications Information Center. Boulder, Colorado: University of Colorado.

Nuttli, O.W., 1981, *Evaluation of Past Studies and Identification of Needed Studies of the Effects of Major Earthquakes Occurring in the New Madrid Fault Zone.* CUSEPP Report No. 81-1 (Preliminary). Kansas City, Missouri: FEMA.

Pewe, T.L. and M.K. Larson, 1982, *Origin of Land Subsidence and Earth Fissures in Northeast Phoenix, Arizona.* City of Phoenix.

Poland, J.F., 1969, *Land Subsidence in the Western United States.* In Olson, R.H. and M.W. Wallace, eds. Geological Hazards and Public Problems Conference Proceedings. Washington, D.C.: U.S. Government Printing Office.

------, 1981, *Subsidence in the United States due to Ground-water Withdrawal.* Journal of the Irrigation and Drainage Division, Proceedings ASCE 107 (1R2):115-135.

Poland, J.R. and J.H. Green, 1962, *Subsidence in the Santa Clara Valley, California--A Progress Report.* Water Supply Paper 1619-C. Washington, D.C.: U.S. Geological Survey.

Poland, J.F. and G.H. Davis, 1969, *Land Subsidence due to Withdrawal of Fluids.* In Varnes, D.J. and G. Kiersch, eds. Reviews in Engineering Geology. Boulder, Colorado: Geological Society of America.

Ruesink L.E., 1977, *Subsidence Costs Analyzed.* Water Research in Action 2(1):2-8.

Seed, H.B. and I.M. Indriss, 1967, *Analysis of Soil Liquefaction: Niigata Earthquake.* Journal of the Soil Mechanics and Foundations Division, Proceedings of the ASCE 93 (Sm-3): 83-108.

Stephens, J.C. and W.H. Spier, 1969, *Subsidence of Organic Soils in the USA.* In Proceedings of the International Symposium on Land Subsidence. Tokoyo, Japan.

Strange, W.E., 1983, *Subsidence Monitoring for State of Arizona.* Rockville, Maryland: U.S. Dept. of Commerce.

U.S. Dept. of Housing and Urban Development, 1977, *The Nature and Distribution of Subsidence Problems Affecting HUD and Urban Areas (Tasks A and E.).* Prepared by the Energy and Natural Resources Program Development, (HRB)-Singer, Inc. Washington, D.C.: U.S. Dept of Housing and Urban Development, Office of Policy Development and Research.

U.S. General Accounting Office, 1979, *Alternatives to Protect Property Owners from Damages Caused by Mine Subsidence.* Report by the Comptroller General, Washington, D.C.: U.S. General Accounting Office.

U.S. Geological Survey, 1983, *Geologic Principles for Prudent Land Use--A Decision Maker's Guide for the San Francisco Bay Region*, Professional Paper 946. Washington, D.C.: U.S. Government Printing Office.

Youd, T.L. and D.K. Keefer, 1981, *Earthquake-Induced Ground Failures.* In W.W. Hays, ed. Facing Geologic and Hydrological Hazards, Earth-Science Considerations. U.S. Geological Survey Professional Paper 1240-B. Washington, D.C.: USGS.

CHAPTER 10: ICE JAM FLOODING

THE HAZARD

An ice jam is an accumulation of floating ice fragments that causes bridging or damming of a river. The flooding caused by ice jams is similar to flash flooding. The formation of a jam results in a rapid rise of water at the point of the jam and upstream. Failure of the jam results in sudden flooding downstream. Flooding as a result of ice jam formation is a problem in 35 out of the 50 states. States particularly prone to such flooding are Alaska, Vermont, Maine, New Hampshire, Washington, Idaho, Minnesota, Wisconsin, Iowa, Illinois and Oregon.

The formation of an ice cover on a river or stream depends upon such factors as flow velocity, turbulence, surface disturbances (wind) and temperature. Successive days of below zero temperatures are often required to form an ice cover on a rapidly flowing stream.

Knowing how ice jams form is the key to knowing when and where to expect them. Ice jam formation depends on both the weather and the physical conditions in the river channel.

Flooding due to ice jams or other ice conditions can occur at different times and in different ways:

1. Ice can cause flooding during fall freeze-up due to the formation of *frazil* ice. Frazil ice forms when temperatures drop but a swift current prevents the formation of an ice cover. Frazil forms in the stream, floats downstream until it reaches an area that is slower moving and frozen over, then attaches itself to the underside of the ice cover. It may accumulate to the point of forming a hanging dam. Frazil can also attach itself to the stream bed, forming *anchor ice.*

2. Ice can cause flooding during mid-winter periods of very low temperature when the stream channel freezes completely solid. Additional water coming down the stream freezes on top of the solid ice until the channel is blocked and the stream flows overland, flooding and freezing on adjacent lands. Solid ice formed in this way frequently blocks culverts.

3. Ice can cause flooding at spring breakup due to a combination of ice conditions creating the classic ice "jam". Most often, rising water levels in the

river or stream from snowmelt and rainfall break the existing ice cover into large chunks. These floating ice masses lodge at bridges or other constrictions, creating dams. Rapid flooding may occur, first upstream, then downstream as the mass of ice and water finally breaks free. Huge ice masses moving downstream can shear off trees and destroy buildings above the level of the flood waters. Damage due to ice is not confined to rivers. On lakes, floating ice masses have been known to shove houses hundreds of feet from their foundations. Pressure ridges, folds formed as ice expands within the confines of the lake banks, can rise several feet above the ice surface.

Damages from ice jam flooding usually exceed those of clear water flooding because of:

1. Higher than predicted flood elevations;

2. Rapid increase in water levels upstream and downstream.

3. Physical damage caused by ice chunks.

EXISTING MITIGATION EFFORTS

Ice jam flooding has not been extensively addressed in flood hazard planning, regulations or management at any level of government. Until recently NFIP flood maps and those prepared by other agencies and states rarely reflected the potential for ice jams. In 1982, the NFIP adopted guidelines for identifying and mapping potential ice jam flooding areas as part of flood insurance studies (see Appendix 10-A). While predicting exactly when and where ice jams will occur is difficult, likely locations can be identified using such an approach.

Research on ice jam flooding has been carried out by the Cold Regions Research Lab of the U.S. Army Corps of Engineers in Dartmouth, New Hampshire. The Corps has also experimented with "ice booms," mechanical removal of ice, and other techniques to reduce ice jam problems.

OPTIONS FOR ACTION

Policy and Program Elements

A community policy and program for ice-related flooding should include the following elements:

1. Adoption of a resolution or policy statement that ice can cause flooding more frequently and at higher levels than the predicted 100-year flood;

2. Mapping of potential ice jam areas such as bridges, natural constrictions in the valley wall as well as potential upstream and downstream inundation areas;

3. Adoption of supplementary regulations including additional setbacks or broadened floodway designations for high velocity flood areas and strengthened performance standards for pilings or floodproofing in flood fringe areas subject to ice-related damages;

4. Installation of warning systems and evacuation plans for areas where serious ice-jam flooding may occur;

5. An analysis of whether remedial engineering measures such as enlargement of culverts or bridge crossings are effective and whether such actions will make ice jam problems greater in other parts of the river;

6. Preparation for short-term remedial actions to clear ice when a jam occurs;

7. Coordination of the activities of floodplain management, transportation and navigation officials.

Mapping

Several options are available to a community in mapping ice jam areas:

1. Map locations potentially susceptible to ice jam flooding and the boundaries of inundation areas using historical evidence of ice jam flooding. Such evidence may include air photos taken during or immediately after the flood while fragments of ice are still present, high water marks, scars on trees, and other physical damage caused by ice. Historic evidence can also be gathered from newspaper archives and interviews with long-term residents. Existing flood maps, topographic maps, air photos, soil maps or other maps may be used as base maps.

2. In the absence of or to supplement historical evidence, carry out engineering studies to identify locations and boundaries of areas subject to inundation. Include subzones within these areas subject to high velocity flows. Federal or state flood-mapping contractors can conduct engineering studies. Potential ice jam and ice damage areas can be identified based upon depth of flow, river profile, valley cross-sections and other factors discussed below.

Modifications to flood maps or the preparation of new maps to reflect ice jam flooding may involve several options:

1. The floodway should be broadened to encompass areas needed to convey flood flows during the jam and adjacent areas threatened by with floating ice.

2. The flood fringe boundaries should be broadened both upstream and downstream of anticipated jam areas to reflect higher flood elevations.

In the last decade technical standards for identifying ice jam inundation areas have improved substantially. Although there are uncertainties in predicting exactly when and where an ice jam will occur, the nature and extent of a possible ice jam at a given location can be anticipated with fair accuracy based on:

1. The anticipated ice thickness;

2. The strength of the ice (estimated by measuring the number of "degree days");

3. The difference between water level just after the formation of a stable ice cover and the water level expected in spring thaw.

The other factor controlling ice jam formation is river morphology (see Figure 11-1). Ice jams typically form:

1. Wherever river slope decreases due either to natural or human causes such as the headwaters of a reservoir.

2. Any constriction in the channel, such as a bend or bridge abutments.

3. Shallow reaches where the ice can freeze to the bottom.

In mapping ice jams as part of broader floodplain mapping efforts designed to identify the 100-year floodplain, the major difficulty is the development of frequency relationships. FEMA's guidelines (Appendix 10-A) describe three possible approaches.

Regulation

Several options are available for strengthening a community's regulations to reduce ice jam damage:

1. Amend floodway maps, as described above, to extend floodway restrictions to the high risk area.

2. As an alternative to a broadened floodway, the high risk areas can be separately zoned as open space through setbacks or open space zoning. Such

LIKELY ICE JAM AREAS

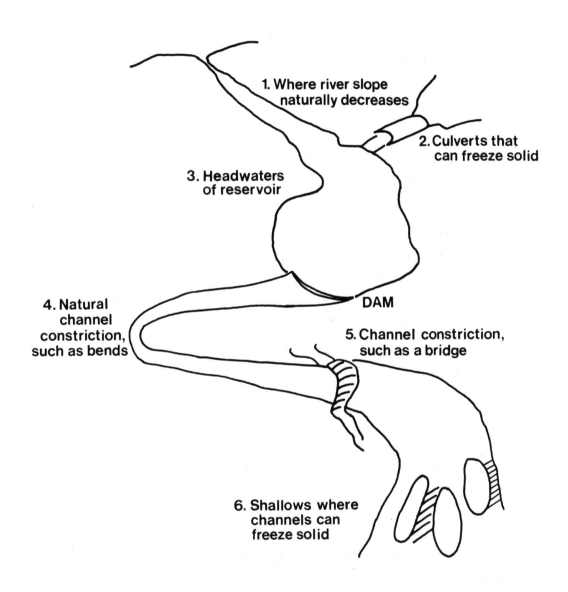

1. Where river slope naturally decreases

2. Culverts that can freeze solid

3. Headwaters of reservoir

DAM

4. Natural channel constriction, such as bends

5. Channel constriction, such as a bridge

6. Shallows where channels can freeze solid

Figure 10-1. Likely ice jam areas.

restrictions can be applied to high velocity flow areas only or to the entire area subject to ice damage.

3.　Add freeboard to protection elevations for structures in flood fringe areas to reflect added heights when jams occur or to protect against damage from floating ice. The amount of freeboard can be based on historic evidence of ice jam inundation or ice damage. For example, a federal hazard mitigation team suggested an added two feet of freeboard in flood fringe areas in response to severe ice jam flooding in Monroe, Michigan.

4.　Amend building codes to include strengthened performance specifications for structures elevated on pilings in high velocity flow or ice damage areas. Alternatively, prohibit pilings altogether in ice jam inundation areas; allow only elevation on fill.

Nonregulatory Options

Principal nonregulatory options include relocation, removal or modification of obstruction, channel modification, ice retention and diversion structures and warning systems. Several case studies are discussed in Appendix 10-B.

Relocation

For areas subject to frequent and severe ice jam flooding and ice damage, acquisition and relocation of structures may be the only permanent way to reduce damages.

Public purchase of land and buildings and relocation of residents are particularly appropriate after an ice jam disaster because ice often totally destroys structures. Relocation is expensive and requires careful planning to be successful. Residents must be involved in the planning as early as possible.

A short-term moratorium on rebuilding after a disaster can facilitate relocation.

Warning Systems and Evacuation Plans

Because of the suddenness of ice jam flooding and the high velocity, ice-laden flows when a jam breaks, a warning system and an evacuation plan similar to those for unsafe dams, levees or other flash flood areas are appropriate.

Removal or Modification of Obstructions

Bridges, culverts, low head dams - even brush and debris in the channel - can cause ice jam flooding. Removing brush and debris and old or obsolete structures may be cost-effective. Rebuilding structures to increase channel capacity and decrease resistance to water and ice flow is another option. For example, replacing a single bridge reduced flood damages by about 80% for two similar flood events in Adams County, North Dakota.

Figure 10-2. This railroad bridge is an example of a man-made structure that can restrict the flow of ice and debris and result in an ice jam. Source: St. Paul District, U.S. Army Corps of Engineers.

Figure 10-3. Large chunks of ice have jammed at a small dam. Source: St. Paul District, U.S. Army Corps of Engineers.

Figure 10-4. The tremendous force of the ice is toppling the tree which
is just to the right of the center of the picture.
Source: Illinois Dept. of Transportation.

Figure 10-5. This house has been protected from flood and ice damage
by being elevated on fill.   Source: Mary Fran Myers.

Channel Modifications

Deepening a channel or straightening a stream can help reduce ice jam problems. The U.S. Army Corps of Engineers is currently studying channel modification as a technique for reducing damage. However this approach is expensive, and dredging is often needed to maintain the new channel configuration. Dredging may even worsen ice jamming downstream because deepened areas allow increased formation of frazil ice in the flowing water which attaches to the bottom of the ice cover downstream.

Ice Retention and Diversion Structures

Diversion channels can divert floodwaters away from the site of jams. The U.S. Army Corps of Engineers Cold Regions Research Laboratory has constructed a physical model for a high level diversion channel.

Piers which retard ice movement or break up ice are a second possibility. The Corps of Engineers has completed this type of project on the Narraguagus River in Cherryfield, Maine.

A third option is an ice retention dam. The Corps has also tried this at the Cherryfield site.

An ice boom is a fourth possibility. An ice boom on the Allegheny River in Oil City, PA controls ice at freeze-up so that ice jamming is minimized at break-up. The boom is submerged at high flows. This approach was used to help protect the Allegheny's wild and scenic river character.

Other Preventative or Remedial Actions

When ice-jamming is likely to occur or has already occurred, several other types of remedial actions are possible to reduce flooding and ice damage. These include dusting, mechanical removal, blasting, controlling the flow of water by surging, and the use of ice breaking ships. See insert.

Dusting

Dusting is the spreading of dark, environmentally safe substances on the ice surface. The dark material absorbs and retains the sun's heat and speeds melting of the ice. Dusting materials must be dry and uniformly sorted. Application is usually from the air which is not always easy on narrow or sinuous rivers. The weather can seriously limit the success of this approach since cloudy skies greatly slow melting and even a slight covering with snow will almost entirely negate the dusting. Despite the difficulties, dusting has been used quite successfully. It was, in fact, the recommended solution for probable ice jam formation in 1984 on the main stem of the Upper Mississippi River.

Mechanical Removal

Construction equipment may be used to mechanically remove jammed ice. If the jam has formed at a bridge, a dragline or backhoe may be used to physically remove blocks of ice from the river. Mechanical removal, while relatively safe, is slow and expensive and only suitable where access is available.

Blasting.

Blasting to break the ice jam can be effective as an emergency technique, but it is also dangerous and can result in downstream flooding. Blasting begins at the head of the jam, where holes are bored through the ice and charges, usually a mixture of ammonium nitrate fertilizer and fuel oil (ANFO), are placed beneath the ice and detonated.

Surging

"Surging" is accomplished by opening and closing the gates of a dam to abruptly change the discharge of the river. The sudden increase in flow velocity and stage may break up a jam. However, if the increased flow is not successful in dislodging the jam, flooding problems can worsen. This method can only be used where control structures exist.

Ice Breaking.

Ships have been used to break up sheet ice. This is a slow, expensive process and most inland rivers are not suited for ice breakers.

Ice Storage.

On smaller streams, it may be possible to use the natural floodplain to "store" ice and prevent jams. Land areas on the outside of bends would be mechanically graded to facilitate the movement of ice onto them during the breakup. Hardwood, Vermont is taking advantage of shallow floodplain areas to store ice to prevent downstream jams. Ice is being held in place by tires tied together by steel cable. The tires and cable are removed during the summer.

Appendix 10-A: Analysis of Ice Jam Flooding excerpts from FEMA's Guidelines and Specifications for Flood Insurance Study Contractors, 1985.

1. INTRODUCTION

An ice jam may be defined as an accumulation of ice in a stream which reduces the cross-sectional area available to carry the flow and increases the watersurface elevation. The accumulation of ice is usually initiated at a natural or manmade obstruction or a relatively sudden change in channel slope, alignment, or cross-section shape or depth. In northern regions of the United States, where rivers can develop relatively thick ice covers during the winter, ice jamming can contribute significantly to flood hazards. When historical records are examined, ice jams are typically found to occur in the same locations. This is because the necessary conditions for genesis of an adequate ice supply and obstruction of its downstream transport determine the specific areas where ice jams will occur. In areas likely to be selected for a detailed FIS, historical documentation is usually available that will indicate if ice jam caused- flooding is a significant factor warranting consideration in the study. In cold regions of the country where ice jams are typical, the Study Contractor should investigate historical floods for evidence of ice jam contribution as part of the study reconnaissance effort. Where ice jams historically contributed to flooding in a community, they should be evaluated using the procedures described in this Appendix (when appropriate).

2. TYPES OF ICE JAMS

Ice jams have been classified in numerous ways by various investigators. Calkins (Reference 1) has classified ice jams as freezeup- or breakup-types, moving or stationary types, and floating or grounded types. Freezeup-type jams are associated with the formation and accumulation of frazil ice, which eventually forms a continuous ice cover. Freezeup-type jams usually do not need to be addressed in a FIS because they are not associated with large discharge events, which are necessary to cause flooding problems. However, the Study Contractor should be aware of possible exceptions. Breakup-type jams are frequently associated with rapid rises in river stage, resulting from rainfall and/or snowmelt, and usually occur in the late winter or early spring. Because of the large volumes of ice that may be involved and the greater discharges associated with them, breakup-type jams are predominant in ice jam-caused flooding and are typically the type requiring investigation in a FIS.

Moving ice does increase water levels; however, these effects are minor compared to those of stationary jams and usually do not need to be considered in a FIS. Floating-type ice jams are considered to be those where the ice is not grounded to the channel bottom and significant flow takes place beneath the ice cover. Grounded-type jams are characterized by an ice cover that is partially grounded to the bed of the channel, with most of the flow being diverted into the overbank and floodplain areas. Grounded-type jams are typical of shallow, confined stream sections, while floating-type jams are typical of deeper rivers. Both of these stationary-type ice jams can cause significant effects and should be addressed in a FIS.

3. RECONNAISSANCE

While conducting the reconnaissance effort for a FIS, the Study Contractor shall detemine whether ice jamming has historically resulted in flooding within the community under study. Where such flooding has occurred, the reconnaissance effort should be intensified to acquire as much data as possible concerning ice jam events in the community, on the streams being studied, and in the region. Such data should include, but not be limited to: locations of ice jams, dimensions, ice volumes, causes, associated river stages discharges, frequency of occurrence, lateral and upstream extent of flooding, season of occurrence, and other contributing or correlative factors. The nature of ice jamming common to the site should also be investigated (i.e.,whether freezeup- or breakup-type jams are typical and whether grounded- or floating-type jams are typical). Because very little documented data are usually available, all possible sources of information must be investigated, including photographs, local residents, newspapers, community officials, State agencies, and Federal agencies.

During the field reconnaissance, the Study Contractor should investigate Physical evidence of ice jams, such as high-water marks, damage to structures or scars on trees, which may provide useful data for the analysis or support for the study results.

4. ANALYSES

Different methods may be used for establishing flood elevations in areas subject to ice jam flooding, depending on the availability of data and the nature of the ice jamming phenomena that occur at the site of interest. The methods outlined herein are applicable primarily to stationary-type (floating or grounded) ice jams that occur during periods of ice breakup. These types of jams have historically resulted in major flooding in certain regions of the United States. The Study Contractor should be aware of conditions that may warrant alternate analytical methods, and should seek approval of alternate methods from the PO before proceeding.

The approaches below are based on the development of stage-frequency relationships for two different populations (ice jam flood stages and free flow flood stages), which are then combined into a single composite curve for flood stages at a site under study. Depending on the availability of ice jam stage information, ice-jam stage-frequency relationships may be determined directly or indirectly as discussed below. The direct method is preferred where applicable.

Direct Approach

If sufficient data exist at the site of interest, an ice-jam stage-frequency distribution can be established directly by fitting a frequency curve to historical ice stage data. This approach is recommended where ice jam stages are available for more than two significant events (i.e., overbank flooding) that span more than a 25-year period of record and where hydraulic conditions have not changed appreciably since those events. Historical stages will permit the computation of plotting positions and fitting a frequency curve on probability paper. Weibull plotting positions are recommended for this purpose.

This approach is preferred over the indirect approaches discussed in the following sections of this Appendix because the joint probabilities of various hydrologic and hydraulic factors, such as discharges, ice volumes, and ice thickness, are inherently included in the frequency analysis.

To apply the direct approach, certain steps should be taken. First, a discharge-frequency curve should be established, using annual peak flows or a suitable regional method, under procedures as required by these Guidelines.

Second, standard hydraulic techniques should be used to establish corresponding free-flow stage-frequency curves for each of the cross sections in the reach where ice jams are to be considered. Usually, the analyses of standard return intervals used in a FIS (i.e., 10-, 50-, 100-, and 500-years) will be sufficient to establish the free-flow stage-frequency curve on normal probability paper.

Third, an ice-jam stage-frequency curve should be established by assigning Weibull plotting positions to historical ice jam stages and fitting a curve to these points on normal probability paper. Fourth, where ice-jam stage-frequency information must be developed for reaches upstream or downstream of the location where a direct analysis can be made, the hydraulic techniques discussed in the following sections on indirect approaches should be used and calibrated to match the ice-jam stage-frequency curve developed for the site with available data. The calibration for floating-type jams would be accomplished by assuming equilibrium ice thickness (as discussed in Section 4b(1)) at the location where the ice-jam stage-frequency curve was developed and by establishing a combination of discharge, equilibrium ice thickness and roughness that would correspond to that stage. The calibration for grounded-type jams would be accomplished by assuming complete blockage of the main channel at the point of obstruction, with equilibrium ice thickness upstream, and then establishing the combination of discharge, equilibrium ice thickness, and roughness that would correspond to that stage. This will permit the HEC-2 ice cover option to be used for estimating corresponding ice jam stages upstream or downstream of the point where historical data are available.

Finally, for each cross section subject to ice jam flooding, the free flow stage-frequency curve, established as described above, must be combined with the ice-jam stage-frequency curve established as described above, assuming the events are independent. Thus,

$$P(s) = P(si) + P(sq) - P(si) \times P(sq)$$

where $P(s)$ = probability of a given stage being equaled or exceeded from either an ice jam event or a free flow event,

$P(si)$ = probability of that stage being equaled or exceeded from an ice jam event,

$P(sq)$ = probability of that stage being equaled or exceeded from a free flow event.

This provides the composite stage-frequency curves at each cross section, which are used to develop flood profiles and maps for the FIS.

Indirect Approaches
(1) Assumptions. The indirect approach to ice-jam stage-frequency analysis may be used where available data are insufficient to establish a stage-frequency distribution directly. This approach makes use of several assumptions:

1. Ice-jam stage frequency is a function of ice jam season discharge frequency.

2. Ice jams are of the breakup type.

3. Ice jams are of the stationary type.

4. For all jams, the ice thickness will be given by the equilibrium relationship developed by Pariset et al. (Reference 2) and the stage-discharge relationship will be determined by adjusting the standard step-backwater technique for flow under an ice cover of equilibrium thickness.

5. For grounded-type jams, the stage-discharge relationship at the point of ice jam formation will be that resulting from complete or nearly complete blockage of the normal channel, with flow being carried in the overbank floodplain areas.

(2) General Procedures. To apply the indirect approach, certain procedures are used. First, a free-flow stage-frequency distribution is established for each cross section by using standard backwater modeling to establish stage-discharge relationships. Usually, the four standard discharges (10-, 50-, 100-, and 500-year return intervals) will provide sufficient points to establish the stage-frequency curve for each cross section on normal probability paper.

The water year is then separated into an "ice jam season" and a "free flow season" based on the historical occurrence of ice jams in the region and, in particular, in the stream under study. The season should encompass the period when breakup-type ice jams normally occur and will likely vary with the latitude and elevation of the stream being studied.

Ice jams tend to be associated with one of the seasonal peak flows because ice jams typically form during rises in river stage that break up the ice sheet. All ice jam season annual peak flows should be fitted to a frequency curve. Weibull plotting positions are recommended for this purpose. For ungaged streams, ice jam season discharge-frequency relationships must be established by regional analysis of seasonal flows for gaged streams. Usually, the establishment of regional ice jam season discharge-drainage area curves will be sufficient for this purpose.

The ice jam season discharge-frequency curve is then converted to a conditional (given that an ice jam occurs) stage-frequency curve. This is done at each cross section subject to ice jam flooding using the HEC-2 program, with the ice cover option. This option takes into account the hydraulic aspects of flow under ice, such as a reduction in flow area, increased wetted perimeter, and ice roughness. Inputs required to utilize this option include the normal HEC-2 input, the thickness of ice in the channel and overbanks, Manning's "n" value for the underside of the ice cover, and the specific gravity of the ice. The Study Contractor is referred to documentaion prepared by the U.S. Army Corps of Engineers; Hydrologic Engineering Center (Reference 3) on the use of this option. The recommended ranges for "n" values are from 0.015 to 0.045 for unbroken ice and from 0.04 to 0.07 for ice jams. The specific gravity of normal ice is approximately 0.92, which is the recommended value for this analysis. Where major floods are caused by ice jams, the assumption of equilibrium ice thickness is probably reasonable because sufficient upstream conditions exist to generate the ice volumes needed. Unless there is strong evidence to the contrary, the ice thickness used in the analysis should be the approximate equilibrium thickness as defined by Pariset et al. (Reference 2). Where equilibrium ice thickness is not appropriate, the Study Contractor should justify the thickness used in the analysis.

The composite stage-frequency curve for establishing the elevations of the various return interval floods at each cross section is then obtained by combining the free-flow stage-frequency distribution and the ice-jam stage-frequency distribution as follows:

$$P(s) = (P(s)|S=F) \times P(S=F) + (P(s)|S=J) \times P(S=J) - ((P(s)|S=F) \times P(S=F)) \times ((P(s)|S=J) \times P(S=J))$$

The probability $(P(s)|S=F)$ is the conditional probability that a given stage(s) is equaled or exceeded given that an annual maximum stage is a free flow event. This conditional probability is the stage-frequency curve for free flow events as derived above. The probability $(S=F)$ is simply the fraction of all annual maximum stages that are free flow events. Likewise, the probability $(P(s)|S=J)$ is the conditional probability that a given stage(s) is equaled or exceeded given that the annual maximum stage is an ice jam event. This conditional probability is obtained as described above. The probability $(S=J)$ is simply the fraction of all annual maximum stages that are ice jam events.

The fraction of annual maximum stages that is attributable to ice jams should then be established through an analysis of historical data at the site, other sites on the same stream and other sites in the region. An analysis of peak stages at gaged sites is often useful for this purpose because peak stages affected by ice are usually documented. Note that, in this indirect procedure, only the relative frequencies of maximum annual stages from ice jam and non-ice jam events need to be estimated. The actual ice jam flood elevation, which is often more difficult to ascertain, is not needed.

The above analysis provides the composite stage-frequency curves for establishing the elevations of the various return interval floods at each cross section. These are then used to establish the flood profiles and floodplain delineations for the FIS.

Grounded Jams

The Study Contractor should document that grounded-type ice jams have occurred historically before grounded-type jam behavior is assumed. The procedures for establishing stage-frequency relationships for stream sections subject to grounded-type ice jamming are identical to those cited earlier except for the hydraulic analysis. Grounded-type jams may occur at confined sections, such as bridges, and at shallow sections. The hydraulic analysis assumes that a high percentage of the normal flow area of the channel (or bridge) is obstructed and that most of the flow is in the overbank areas.

Hydraulic effects at the point of obstruction and upstream should be modeled using step-backwater methods modified for ice cover. The U.S. Army Corps of Engineers' HEC-2 program, with the ice cover option, is recommended for this purpose (Reference 3). At the point of obstruction, the use of an actual or hypothetical bridge section will permit the special bridge routine to be used to facilitate the analysis. The low chord of the bridge (HEC-2 variable ELLC) and the net flow area (HEC-2 variable BAREA) may then be adjusted to achieve different degrees of blockage of the main channel. The Study Contractor should normally assume between 95 and 100 percent blockage of the channel unless sufficient evidence exists to support another assumption. In that case, the alternative should be documented and justified. Upstream from the site of grounding, equilibrium ice thickness, as computed according to the Pariset formulation (Reference 2), should be assumed unless alternate thicknesses can be justified.

5. PRESENTATION OF RESULTS

FIS Report

A discussion of historic ice jam flooding should appear in Section 2.3 (Principal Flood Problems) of the FIS report.

Section 3.1 (Hydrologic Analyses) of the report should include a discussion of any discharge-frequency analysis for the ice jam season, if used. Similarly, the statistical treatment of stage-frequency analyses for ice jam and non-ice jam events should be discussed. The historical data used in the analyses should be referenced in the discussion along with its source and how it was used. The Summary of Discharges Table should be based on analysis of the full year and footnoted to that effect.

Section 3.2 (Hydraulic Analyses) of the FIS report should include a discussion of how free flow and ice jam stages were computed, whether stages were computed directly from stage-frequency analyses or indirectly analyzed. The approximate channel blockage and ice thickness assumed should be discussed, if used. The relationship of the computed ice jam stages to historic floods should be discussed. An example of stage-frequency curves for combined floods should be provided for the point of obstruction, or a representative cross section within the community should be provided if the former is outside the corporate limits. The discussion should also indicate that floodways were computed only for free flow conditions.

The "Regulatory" column of the Floodway Data Table should be prepared using the 100-year flood elevations established from the composite ice-jam and free-flow season stage-frequency curves and footnoted to that effect. All other columns in the Floodway Data Table shall be based on the 100-year free flow conditions.

Profiles

The flood profiles shown in the FIS shall be based on the elevations established from the composite ice-jam and free-flow stage-frequency analysis.

Maps

FIRM shall be developed based on the elevations established from the composite ice-jam and free-flow stage-frequency analyses performed at each cross section. Floodways shall be established and plotted based on the 100-year flood discharges and hydraulics assuming free flow conditions. The lateral extent of a major historic ice jam may be indicated on the work map if it is well documented, does not hamper interpretation, and is appropriately annotated as such.

6. REFERENCES

1. U.S. Army Cold Regions Research and Engineering Laboratory, Technical Note, *Methodology for Ice Jam Analysis*, D. J. Calkins, October 1980.

2. E. Pariset, R. Hausser, and A. Gagnon, *Formation of Ice Covers and Ice Jams in Rivers.* Journal of the Hydraulics Division, ASC,. November 1966.

3. U.S. Army Corps of Engineers. Hydrologic Engineering Center, *Analysis of Flow in Ice Covered Streams Using Computer Program HEC-2*, February 1979.

Appendix 10-B: Cold Facts of Ice Jams: Case Studies of Mitigation Methods

Extracted from a paper by Darryl J. Calkins, Research Hydraulic Engineer at USACRREL, presented at the 8th Annual Conference of the Association of State Floodplain Managers, 1984.

CASE STUDIES

The following case studies represent several types of ice-related flood problems. In some cases solutions were recommended and implemented, while others are still in the evaluation or design phase.

1.   Allegheny River

Report: Ice Jam Problems at Oil City, PA, by Deck and Gooch, USACRREL Special Report 81-9.

Location: Oil City, PA

Problems: Ice jam flooding at the confluence of Oil Creek and the Allegheny River.

Cause: A river dredging project on the Allegheny created a deep, long pool just downstream of the confluence with Oil Creek, which caused a large ice accumulation to occur. The ice run from the smaller tributary could not penetrate the Allegheny River ice cover. The ice jam would remain in the tributary channel and the floodplain (Oil City Business district) would handle the flow.

Solution: Winter field investigations revealed an excessive ice build-up - 15 feet at the confluence during freeze-up. A relatively inexpensive ice boom just upstream of the confluence was designed to start the freeze-up ice cover at that location and minimize the ice volume at the confluence area.

Implemented: 1982

Performance: Ice volumes have been dramatically reduced. Although conditions have been favorable for ice jam formation, no ice jam flooding has occurred, as the tributary ice run can now move into the main river.

2. Salmon River

Reports: a) Special Flood Hazard Information   - Salmon River Ice Jams, February 1984, USACE - Walla Walla District.

     b) Salmon River Ice Jams, 1984, by Cunningham and Calkins, ASCE Hydraulics Division Specialty Conference, Coeur d'Alene, ID.

Location: Salmon, ID

Problem: Ice jam flooding at freeze-up and break-up on both the mainstem river and a tributary.

Background: The river is designated as wild and scenic. Hydraulic mining activities created the problem in late 1800's by altering the natural channel characteristics of the Salmon River 26 miles downstream of Salmon, Idaho. Winter river observations will be expanded to analyze the environmental impact and to assess performance of the possible alternatives with respect to the ice regime.

Causes: a) Thick ice cover formation results in stage increases of 8 - 12 ft; low temperatures must occur in the basin.

            b) Floodplain encroachment.

            c) Break-up ice conditions occur with a higher flow discharge, which creates even higher stages; mild weather must occur to create high flows.

Solutions: Alternatives are being evaluated under the 205 program.

3. Israel River

Reports: a) Israel River Ice Jam, by Frankenstein and Assur, 1972 IAHR Symposium on Ice, Leningrad, pp. 153-157.

            b) Detailed Project Report - Israel River, NED-COE, Waltham, MA.

Location: Lancaster, NH.

Problem: Break-up ice jam flooding in the business district and some residential areas.

Causes: a) Removal of two old mill dams upstream of the flooding area.

            b) The flooding area is located at the transition from steep to mild slope.

            c) A thick accumulation of ice develops in the mild slope reach during freeze-up, reducing break-up ice storage.

Solution: Install submarine net 1 mile above the flooded area where the river changed slope and floodplain relief for water and ice was available.

Implemented: 1974.

Performance: The structure has held back ice each year, primarily because floodplain relief for the water is available. This was a good solution for holding back ice at this location. However, the 1 mile of ice between the net and the town was still sufficient to cause ice jams in the flooded area.

Solution: Construct a low head weir 0.5 mile upstream of the flooding area near the site of the first old mill dam to serve as a replacement.

Implemented: 1982.

Performance: The structure does not hold back ice, as the pool length is too short. Ice jam flooding still exists. Additional modifications may be necessary.

4. Delaware River

Reports: a) General Investigation Report in preparation, Sept. 84, Philadelphia District, COE.

b) Preliminary Ice Jam Study - Delaware River, by Calkins, Report submitted to Philadelphia District, June 1984.

Location: Port Jervis, NY - Matamorous, PA.

Problem: Break-up ice jam flooding in above communities.

Causes: Not fully understood yet; only three major events have occurred in the last 110 years, with the jam of record occurring in 1981, which caused $18 million in damage. A midwinter jam at Port Jervis followed by the spring break-up appear to be causes of this flood.

Solution: Several alternatives are being considered.

a) Permanent hydraulic structure.

b) Flow control, freeze-up and break-up.

c) Ice control at freeze-up with ice booms.

d) High-level diversion channels.

e) Levee protection.

5. Peace River

Report: a)Freeze-up flood stages associated with fluctuating reservoir releases, by Neill and Adres, 3rd Specialty Conference on Cold Regions Engineering, April 4-6, 1984, Edmonton, Alberta.

b) Several other references cited in the above paper for same site.

Location: Peace River, Alberta, Canada

Problem: Freeze-up ice cover flooding.

Causes: a) Construction of hydropower dam 100 miles upstream.

b) Release schedule of flow (surges).

c) Increased winter flows versus the natural condition (factor of 2-3).

Solution: Modify release schedule during freeze-up.

Implemented: Some modification of the releases.

Performance: Insufficient data have been collected.

6. Chaudiere River

Report: a) Projects to alleviate ice jams on the Chaudiere River, by Deslauriers, Proceedings of Eastern Snow Conference 1965, pp. 115-127.

              b) Ice control structures for river break-up, by Michel, Proceedings, 11th Congress of IAHR 1965, Vol. 5, pp. 37-48.

Location: Quebec.

Problem: Ice jam flooding at break-up.

Causes: a) Thick ice accumulations at freeze-up.

              b) No river channel storage at break-up for the ice due to freeze-up of thick ice.

Solution: Construct a 60-ft-high dam upstream of the flooded area.

Implemented: 1967.

Performance: Ice jam flooding occurs now in the pool behind the structure and not in the community. It is considered very successful.

SELECTED REFERENCES ON FLOODING DUE TO ICE JAMS

Ashton, G.D., 1978, River Ice. *Ann. Rev. Flood Mech.* 10:369-92.

------,1979, River Ice. *American Scientist* 67(1):38-45.

Bates, Roy and Mary Lynn Brown, 1982, *Meterological Conditions Causing Major Ice Jam Formation and Flooding on the Ottawgucchee River, Vermont.* Special Report 82-6. Washington, D.C.: U.S. Army Corps of Engineers Cold Regions Research and Engineering Laboratory.

Billfalk, L., 1982, *Breakup of Solid Ice Covers Due to Rapid Water Level Variations.* Special Report 82-03. Washington, D.C.: U.S. Army Corps of Engineers Cold Regions Research and Engineering Laboratory.

Calkins, D., 1980, *Methodology for Ice Jam Analysis.* Technical Note. Washington, D.C.: U.S. Army Corps of Engineers Cold Regions Research and Engineering Laboratory.

-----1984, Personal Communication.

Deck, D. and G. Gooch, 1981, *Ice Jam Problems at Oil City, Pennsylvania.* Special Report 81-9. Washington, D.C.: U.S. Army Corps of Engineers Cold Regions Research and Engineering Laboratory.

Donahue and Associates, Inc., 1982, *Flood Control Feasibility Study for City of Fond du Lac, Wisconsin,* Report to the City.

Federal Emergency Management Agency, 1982, *Guidelines and Specifications for Flood Insurance Studies,* Appendix C: Analysis of Ice Jam Flooding. Washington, D.C.: FEMA.

Gerard, R., 1980, *Notes for a Short Course on Ice Engineering for Rivers and Lakes.* University of Wisconsin Extension.

Killaby, H.H., 1887, *The Work on the River Missouri at St. Joseph.* Transactions of the Canadian Society of Civil Engineers 1:48-67.

Pariset, E., R. Hausser and A. Gagnon, 1966, *Formation of Ice Covers and Ice Jams in Rivers.* Journal of the Hydraulics Division, Proceedings of the ASCE 92: 11-19.

U.S. Army Corps of Engineers, 1975, *CRREL Technical Publications,* Washington, D.C.: Cold Regions Research and Engineering Laboratory.

------,1979, *Analysis of Flow in Ice Covered Streams Using Computer Program HEC-2.* Washington, D.C.: Hydrologic Engineering Center.

------,1980, Section 206 *Floodplain Management Assistance Historical Ice Jam Flooding in Maine, New Hampshire and Vermont*. Washington, D.C.: New England Division, Corps of Engineeers.

------1980, Special Flood Hazard Information: *Snake River Ice Jams*. Walla Walla, Washington, Walla Walla District. Corps of Engineers.

------,1981, *CRREL Technical Publications, Supplement 1 January 1976 to 1 July 1981*. Washington, D.C.: Cold Regions Research and Engineering Laboratory.

------1982, *Ice Engineering. Engineering Manual No. 1110-2-1612*. Washington, D.C.: Corps of Engineers.

------1983, *CRREL Technical Publications, Supplement 1 July 1981 to 1 February 1983*. Washington, D.C.: Cold Regions Research and Engineering Laboratory.

CHAPTER 11: MUDSLIDES

THE HAZARD

Mudfloods and mudflows are a major problem in sparsely vegetated mountains or hilly areas of the West and Southwest with low rainfall and unconsolidated soils. When rains do occur, runoff is rapid due to the lack of vegetative cover. Moving water quickly picks up soil and rock particles. The resulting mixtures of water and sediment range from muddy water to partly solid "mudslides". Although primarily a western problem, mudfloods and mudflows occur in Appalachia and elsewhere.

Mudflows and mudfloods are often caused, in part, by rain falling on terrain that has been denuded by forest fires and brush fires. Once denuded, hills do not retain runoff. Even small rainfalls can cause flash-flooding.

MUDFLOOD AND MUDFLOW

The National Academy of Science (1983) suggested the following definitions for these terms:

Mudflood: Refers to a flood in which the water carries heavy loads of sediment (as much as 50% by volume) including coarse debris. Mudfloods typically occur in drainage channels and on alluvial fans adjacent to mountainous regions, although they may occur on flood-plains as well.

Mudflow: Refers to a specific subset of landslides where the dominant transporting mechanism is that of a flow having sufficient viscosity to support large boulders within a matrix of smaller sized particles. Mudflows may be confined to drainage channels or may occur unconfined on hillslopes.

There are no reliable estimates of the annual cost of damage due to mudfloods or mudflows. Los Angeles County has estimated over 2 million individuals may be at risk from mud and other debris flows in this county alone. Estimates of total damage caused by landslides, of which mudslides are a substantial component, range up to one billion dollars a year. Recent floods in the west and southwest have had large mudflood and mudflow damage components.

Mudflows and mudfloods start with moving water or a stationary mass of saturated soil. Mudfloods usually originate as sheet flow or as water flowing in drainage channels, rivers or streams. Waters pick up sediment or debris as they flow. In contrast, mudflows often originate as a mixture of stationary soil and water. When the mixture gets wet enough it begins to move as a mass, either on its own (by force of gravity) or triggered by another event (such as an earthquake or a sudden flow of debris laden water). See Figures 11-1 and 11-2.

Sediment-laden waters and mudflows cause more severe damage than clear water flooding for several reasons. The force of debris-laden water can be hundreds of times greater than clear water, destroying pilings and other protective works. Structures are often totally destroyed. The mud and debris may fill drainage channels and sediment basins, causing floodwaters to suddenly inundate areas outside of the floodplain. The combination of sediment and debris is more damaging to buildings and their contents than clear water. Even where structures remain intact, sediment often severely damages or destroys rugs and contents and must be physically removed with shovels or hoses. Repeated washings are needed and stains are often permanent.

EXISTING MITIGATION EFFORTS

Mudflows and mudfloods have not been extensively mapped, regulated or otherwise managed at federal, state or local levels. The most innovative and hazard-specific regulation has been undertaken by the State of Colorado and a number of communities in California, including Los Angeles County. Some regulations have also been adopted in Utah.

Federal

The U.S. Geological Survey has studied mudflows and other debris flows quite extensively and has prepared reports to their identification and management. It has mapped potential mudflow and mudslide areas in the San Francisco Bay Region, along the Wasatch front near Salt Lake City (see Figure 11-3), and in the Appalachian region. The U.S.G.S. has recently proposed a national landslide reduction program which would include mudflood and mudflow phenomenon.

In 1969 Congress amended the National Flood Insurance Act by expanding the definition of flood to include "mudslide" and to authorize FIA mapping and flood insurance for "mudslide" areas. Pursuant to this mandate, FIA undertook some experimental mapping in Los Angeles County, California, adopted regulatory guidelines for local regulation of mudslide areas (see Appendix 11-A) and requested the National Research Council to help develop a more detailed mapping methodology. In 1974, the Council recommended a general susceptibility approach for delineating areas based on topographic, soil and geologic factors. However, FIA considered this approach inadequate to meet legal requirements. In 1980, FEMA asked the Research Council to evaluate the general applicability of the methodology that had been applied in Los Angeles County. This study concluded that the methodology was not transferable to other locations.

State

In 1974, the Colorado legislature adopted a land planning act designed to assist local governments manage areas of state interest. Areas of state interest were defined include geologic hazard areas subject to a "geologic phenomenon which is so adverse to past, current or foreseeable construction or land use as to constitute a significant hazard to public health or safety or to property." The statute listed these specific hazards:

1. Avalanche,
2. Landslides,
3. Rock falls,
4. Mudflows and debris fans,
5. Unstable or potentially unstable slopes,
6. Seismic effects,
7. Radioactivity,
8. Ground subsidence,
9. Expansive soil and rock.

The Colorado Geological Survey was directed to help local governments identify geologic hazard areas and adopt management guidelines. In carrying out this task, the Survey has prepared guidelines and a number of excellent reports which may be of interest to other states including Guidelines and Criteria for Identification and Land-Use Controls for Geologic Hazard and Mineral Resource Areas (Colorado, Geological Survey, 1979; see Appendix 3-D).

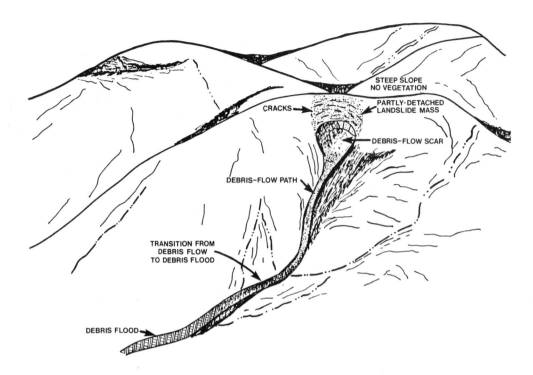

Figure 11-1. Debris may begin to flow as a mass when it becomes wet. Gravity, earthquakes or a sudden flow of debris-laden water could be the triggering mechanism.   Source: U.S.G.S.

Figure 11-2. Recent land failure is evident.   Source: Jon Kusler.

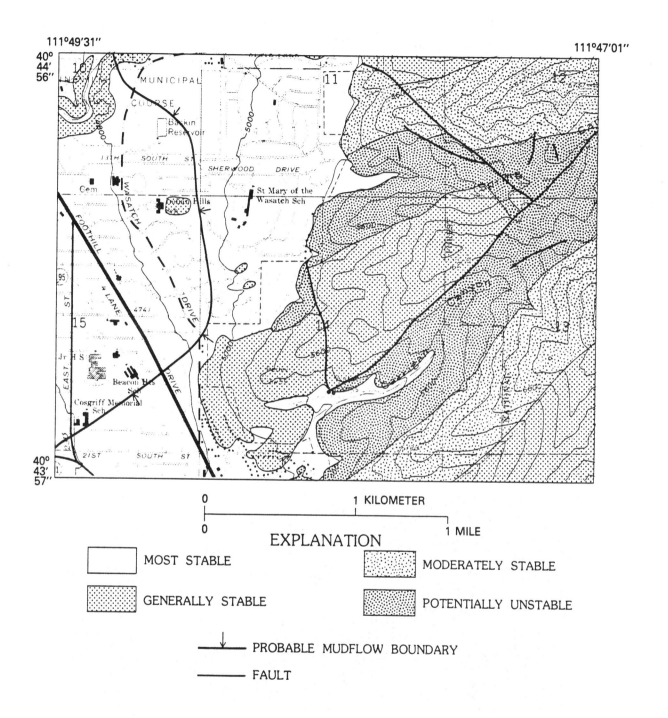

Figure 11-3. Mudslide susceptibility near Salt Lake City, Utah. "The features considered in preparing the relative slope stability map include: steepness of slope, type of rock or surficial deposit, and locations of bedrock, faults, springs, and former marshes. These features were evaluated according to their relation to known landslide deposits and talus accumulations, to the observed deterioration of buildings in the area, and, in small part, to plausible predictions." Source: U·S.G.S

The State Geological Surveys in California and Utah also helped communities regulate mudslide areas by preparing maps indicating geologic, seismic and slope stability problems.

Local

Several dozen communities now regulate development in mudflows, mudflood areas or broader debris flow areas. Some of the most interesting include:

Los Angeles County, California has developed a method for identifying mudflood and other debris areas. Using records of debris flow compiled over a 40-year period, the County Flood Control District has determined potential flooding and debris volume for each major canyon in the area. Applying a 50-year frequency rainfall standard in a "burned watershed" computation, the District has prepared mudflood maps. The District reviews all tract and building plans in mapped areas (see Appendix 11-B). All developments must be designed to accommodate expected water and debris.

San Bernardino, California. As a result of a 1979 forest fire in Harrison Canyon north of San Bernardino, four mudflows occurred in the city in 1980, damaging 30 structures. After the third, the city passed an emergency ordinance prohibiting repair of damaged structures and began to acquire these structures. Assisted by FEMA with funding from the Section 1362 Program, the City has acquired 26 structures. It has also implemented erosion control measures in the upper canyon and constructed retaining walls in the lower areas.

OPTIONS FOR COMMUNITY ACTION

Policy and Program Elements

A community with mudflood and mudflow problems should adopt a mitigation policy and program with the following elements:

> 1. A policy statement or resolution that mudfloods or mudflows create severe risks to life and property;
>
> 2. Mapping of mudflood and mudflow areas as part of a flood mapping program or as part of a broader geologic hazards or resource management effort;

3. Adoption of regulations requiring slope stability analysis and either prohibiting development in unstable areas or establishing performance guidelines for new development;

4. Notification of landowners in potential mudslide areas; and

5. Preparation and implementation of plans for remedial action such as debris basins and dewatering of unstable slopes.

Mapping

The National Flood Insurance maps often include (but do not specifically indicate) mudflood areas along major streams. Mudflow and mudslide areas on valley slopes and along smaller rivers and streams have rarely been mapped. As indicated earlier, the U.S. Geological Survey has mapped areas subject to potential mudflows and other debris flows in the San Francisco Bay area, along the Wasatch front near Salt Lake City and in the Appalachian region.

Two approaches are available for communities without maps or where maps do not specifically indicate mudflow or mudflood problems. The first is to prepare of special maps indicating hazards. For example, Los Angeles County has prepared its own maps based upon soils, topography and slope. The second is to shift the burden to developers to assess hazards in areas within a defined distance of water course or on slopes greater than a defined amount (e.g., 15%). The latter approach is used more often. Relative slope stability categories are given in Appendix 11-F; these categories help identify potential mudflow areas, but are less useful in the delineation of mudflood areas.

Regulations

Two principal regulatory approaches have been applied to date:

1. Prohibition of all new development on slopes through setbacks or open space zoning for high risk areas.

2. Adoption of performance standards for fill, grading, or design of structures.

Los Angeles County, California takes the latter approach. Building and grading codes permit building on slope areas only under these conditions:

1. It does not increase water depths on neighboring lands;

2. It does not deflect water onto neighboring properties;

3. Structures are designed to withstand the force of anticipated flows.

Developers must conduct geologic studies and design structures consistent with the regulatory guidelines. According to a study conducted by Slossen and Krohn, the ordinance has reduced slope failures since adoption (see Table 11-1). See Appendices for portions of the Los Angeles grading code (see Appendix 11-B) and excerpts from ordinances of Whittier and Ventura, California (Appendices 11-C and 11-D). See also Appendix 11-E for excerpts from the Uniform Building Code which pertain to cuts and fills.

Table 11-1 Slope Failures in the City of Los Angeles (1978 storms)

Description	Number of Sites	Number of Failures	Percent Failure	Dollar Value (millions)
Pre-1963 (before modern code)	37,000	2,790	7.5	40-49
Post-1963 (modern code)	30,000	210	0.7	1-2

Note: The categories of failure are (1) soil slippage and erosion (28 percent); (2) mudflow and debris flow (30 percent); (3) slump/arcuate landslides, pre-1963 and natural slopes (22 percent); (4) reactivation of old failures, pre-1963 (8 percent); (5) new bedrock landslides, pre-1963 (5 percent); (6) shallow fill slope and some natural slope failure, post-1963 (7 percent, with the modern code promulgated in April 1963).

Source: Slosson and Krohn (1979).

Nonregulatory Actions

Principal nonregulatory actions to reduce hazards in mudflow and mudflood areas include debris basins, acquisition and planting and other soil conservation measures.

Debris Basins

Debris basins resemble dry reservoirs and operate in much the same way. They are used extensively in Los Angeles County and some other western communities to trap debris flows. The Japanese depend on an estimated 200,000 of these structures.

Debris basins are costly but they are effective in reducing mud damage. Debris trapped in the basins must be periodically removed by mechanical means to maintain the basin's effectiveness.

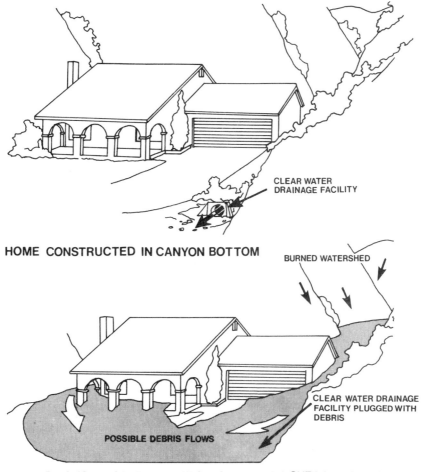

HOME CONSTRUCTED IN CANYON BOTTOM

CLEAR WATER DRAINAGE FACILITY

BURNED WATERSHED

CLEAR WATER DRAINAGE FACILITY PLUGGED WITH DEBRIS

POSSIBLE DEBRIS FLOWS

HOME CONSTRUCTED IN BOTTOM OF CANYON OVERRUN BY DEBRIS

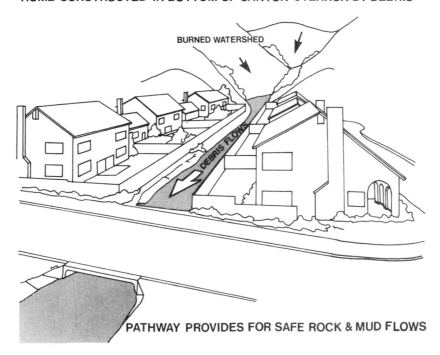

BURNED WATERSHED

DEBRIS FLOWS

PATHWAY PROVIDES FOR SAFE ROCK & MUD FLOWS

Figure: 11-4. Design and construction standards can be applied to reduce risk to structures.

Other Engineering Approaches

Other engineering solutions to mudflow problems include retaining walls and "dewatering" of soils through horizontal wells, subsurface drains and other techniques.

Acquisition

As noted above, San Bernardino, California used acquisition to remove structures from a high risk mudflow area. Acquisition has also been used "preventatively" in some Los Angeles County canyons to acquire undeveloped land for park and recreation purposes and to reduce future damage potential.

Planting and Other Soil Conservation Measures

San Bernardino stabilized hillsides in newly burned areas through replanting, the placement of straw and other slope stabilization techniques. Application of such techniques, both pre- and post-disaster, has broad potential for reducing future damages from newly burned areas.

Land Owner Education

Buyers, builders and homeowners should be provided with information concerning potential hazard areas. See Appendix 11-F.

Appendix 11-A Criteria of the Federal Emergency Management Agency for Community Participation in the National Flood Insurance Program.

...Floodplain management criteria for mudslide (i.e., mudflow)-prone areas.

The Administrator will provide the data upon which floodplain management regulations shall be based. If the Administrator has not provided sufficient data to furnish a basis for these regulations in a particular community, the community shall obtain, review, and reasonably utilize data available from other Federal, State or other sources pending receipt of data from the Administrator. However, when special mudslide (i.e., mudflow) hazard designations have been furnished by the Administrator, they shall apply. The symbols defining such special mudslide (i.e., mudflow) hazard designations are set forth in 64.3 of this subchapter. In all cases, the minimum requirements for mudslide (i.e., mudflow)-prone areas adopted by a particular community depend on the amount of technical data provided to the community by the Administrator. Minimum standards for communities are as follow:

(a)   When the Administrator has not yet identified any area within the community as an area having special mudslide (i.e. mudflow) hazards, but the community has indicated the presence of such hazards by submitting an application to participate in the Program, the community shall:

    (1)   Require permits for all proposed construction or other development in the community so that it may determine whether development is proposed within mudslide (i.e., mudflow)-prone areas;

    (2)   Require review of each permit application to determine wheter the proposed site and improvements will be reasonably safe from mudslides (i.e., mudflows). Factors to be considered in making such a determination should include but not be limited to (i) the type and quality of soils, (ii)any evidence of ground water or surface water problems, (iii) the depth and quality of any fill, (iv) the overall slope of the site, and (v) the weight that any proposed structure will impose on the slope;

    (3)   Require, if a proposed site and improvements are in a location that may have mudslide (i.e., mudflow) hazards, that (i) a site investigation and further review be made by persons qualified in geology and soils engineering, (ii) the proposed grading, excavations, new construction, and substantial improvements are adequately designed and protected against mudslide (i.e. mudflow) damages, (iii) the proposed grading, excavations, new construction and substantial improvements do not aggravate the existing hazard by creating either on-site or off-site disturbances, and (iv) drainage, planting, watering, and maintenance be such as not to endanger slope stability.

(b)   When Administrator has delineated Zone M on the community's FIRM, the community shall:

    (1)   Meet the requirements of paragraph (a) of this section; and

    (2)   Adopt and enforce a grading ordinance or regulation in accordance with data supplied by the Administrator which (i) regulates the location of foundation systems and utility systems of new construction and substantial improvements, (ii) regulates the location, drainage and maintenance of all ex-

cavations, cuts and fills and planted slopes, (iii) provides special requirements for protective measures including but not necessarily limited to retaining walls, buttress fills, subdrains, diverter terraces, benchings, etc., and (iv) requires engineering drawings and specifications to be submitted for all corrective measures,, accompanied by supporting soils engineering and geology reports. Guidance may be obtained from the provisions of the 1973 edition and any subsequent edition of the Uniform Building Code, sections 7001 through 7006, and 7008 through 7015. The Uniform Building Code is published by the International Conference of Building Officials, 50 South Los Robles, Pasadena, California 91109.

Appendix 11-B: Excerpts from the City of Los Angeles Official Grading Regulations.

DEPARTMENT OF BUILDING AND SAFETY, CITY OF LOS ANGELES BUILDING BUREAU, RULE OF GENERAL APPLICATION--RGA 4-67

From James E. Slosson and James P. Krohn, "Southern California Landslides of 1978 and 1980" in Storms, Floods, and Debris Flows in Southern California and Arizona in 1978 and 1980, Proceedings of a Symposium, September 17-18, 1980, National Academy Press, Washington, D.C.

Subject: Rules and Regulations for Supervision on Hillside Tract Grading--RR 23352

The permittee shall employ a registered civil engineer or land surveyor to prepare his design of grading plans for all hillside grading. The design civil engineer or land surveyor shall prepare his design in accordance with good planning practice, applicable Codes and to the restrictions imposed thereon as determined by detailed studies of the site and materials to be graded. These studies shall be performed by a soils engineer and an engineering geologist approved by the City of Los Angeles and shall be submitted prior to issuance of permits. The design civil engineer or land surveyor shall furnish sufficient supervision during construction to obtain compliance with the plans, as approved.

The permittee shall employ a soils engineer and an engineering geologist prior to planning the tract, whose duties shall be: to work closely with the design civil engineer or land surveyor, to examine surface and subsurface conditions in accordance with the Rule of General Application dealing with "Subsurface Exploratory Work" and to submit reports thereon. These reports, in conjunction with the Ordinance, shall form the basis for the design of the grading project. These reports shall be based upon a detailed topographic base map of the area to be graded and shall include specific conclusions and recommendations for avoidance or correction of all known existing or anticipated geologic hazards on or affecting the site or contiguous property.

The soils engineer, in addition to his pre-grading exploratory work, shall provide inspection during the placement of all compacted fill in accordance with the requirement of the Ordinance, the approved plans and good engineering practice. In addition, he shall follow the progress of the job sufficiently close to determine that the recommendations of his pre-grading report are followed. If conditions which require modification of plans are encountered during grading, he shall submit a report of his findings and recommendations for change of plans to the permittee and the design civil engineer, the engineering geologist and the department.

The engineering geologist, in addition to his pre-grading exploratory work, shall provide inspection during the actual grading process at least as often as determined to be appropriate by the Department or Board, with periodic in-grading inspection reports submitted at intervals determined by the Department. Such grading inspection by the engineering geologist is to determine that the conditions of his pre-grading report are as anticipated. If conditions which require modification of the plans are encountered during grading, he shall submit a report of his findings and recommendations to the committee, design civil engineer or land surveyor, soils engineer and the Department.

The soils engineer, at the completion of grading, shall submit a certified report of compaction tests for all fill located within the limits of the tract and/or offsite grading areas.

The soils engineer's final report shall also include: a statement that all sub-drains were installed, his professional opinion of the suitability of the fill placement area and the ability of the natural materials to support the compacted fill without excessive settlement of the fill or potential damage to structures erected thereon, a statement to the effect that he has inspected all cuts and fills and that in his opinion they meet the design requirements. The report shall be referenced to a dated as-graded plan prepared by the design civil engineer or land surveyor.

The engineering geologist at the completion of grading shall submit a final geologic report stating that: he had maintained the required in-grading inspection, the recommendations of his pre-grading report(s) have been followed, that in his professional opinion all known adverse geologic conditions have been corrected or provided for, future adverse geologic conditions are not anticipated, and all lots or sites are geologically suitable and safe for construction. The report shall include the geologist's certification that he has inspected all cut slopes and sidehill fill placement areas prior to placement of fill. He shall also certify that all sub-drain placement areas were inspected prior to installation of the sub-drains. The report shall be referenced to a dated as-graded plan prepared by the design civil engineer or land surveyor.

Upon completion of grading, the civil engineer or land surveyor responsible for the design shall submit an as-graded plan to the Department for approval of all work covered by the grading permit(s) and shall include the following:
1. The plan shall be at a 1 inch = 40 feet scale and shall show the locations of streets, pads, slopes, structures, pertinent elevations, original contours and finished elevations, other pertinent information required to show the as-graded condition, and shall be dated.
2. The plan shall bear the signature of the design civil engineer or land surveyor which shall certify that he has inspected the site, reviewed the plans and that the work shown and completed is in accordance with his design.

If, for any reason any of the three professional persons is terminated during the progress of the grading work, he and the committee shall immediately notify the Department in writing. Such termination may result in temporary delays in the grading operations until satisfactory arrangements are made to assure the Department that competent professional supervision is provided. When one or all three of the professionals of record are terminated, the new professional(s) shall submit to the Department a letter of certification that the previous professional's designs, reports and recommendations have been reviewed, all provisions of the Board or Department required as conditions of the grading permit will be complied with during the course of the work, and he or they shall review the detailed 40-scale grading plans and thus assume his or their responsibility as herein specified for all future grading on the project. The letters shall be referenced to the approved grading plans prepared by the design civil engineer or land surveyor.

The certification submitted by the civil engineer or land surveyor shall pertain to the tract as built. The certification shall apply to the angle of stability of cut and fill slopes, compaction requirements, drainage provisions, and in general, all safety features incorporated in a well-graded hillside job. Engineers and geologists employed for the development shall not be deemed to be responsible for the work if alteration work not under their control is undertaken after the grading certificate has been issued

RULE OF GENERAL APPLICATION--RGA 5-67

Subject: Regulations for Hillside Exploratory Work--RR 23353

The following rules and regulations shall apply on required hillside surface and subsurface exploratory work:

Surface and subsurface exploratory work shall be performed by a soils engineer and an engineering geologist approved by the City of Los Angeles on all hillside grading work, except wherein waived by the Department Staff or Board, Such exploratory work shall be performed for the purpose of obtaining detailed information on which the soils engineer and the engineering geologist shall base recommendations for a grading project. The work shall be based upon a detailed, accurate topographic base map prepared by the registered civil engineer or land surveyor. The map shall be of suitable scale, and shall cover the area to be graded, as well as adjacent areas which may be affected by the grading. The map shall include the existing and proposed contours, locations of streets, pads, slopes, structures, and pertinent elevations.

The engineering geologist's and soils engineer's exploratory work shall be conducted at locations considered most likely to reveal any subsurface weaknesses which may lead to landslide, slump or settlement failures. Particularly, an investigation shall be conducted where the stability will be lessened by the grading or where any of the following conditions are discovered or proposed:

1. At fault zones where past land movement is evidenced by the presence of fault gouge.
2. At contact zones between two or more geologic formations. 3. At zones of trapped water or high water table quite often associated with conditions 1 and 2 above.
4. At bodies of intrusive materials.
5. At historic landslides or where the topography is indicative of prehistoric landslides.
6. At adversely sloped bedding planes, short range folding, overturned folds, etc.
7. At locations where a fill slope is to be placed above a cut slope.
8. At proposed cuts exceeding 25 feet in height unless in competent rock or of lesser heights in rock of questionable stability.
9. At the locations of all proposed fills.
10. Where any side hill fills are proposed.
11. Wherever water from rainfall, irrigation, private sewage disposal systems, or other probable sources from both the grading project and adjoining properties is likely to reduce the subsurface stability.
12. Where the proposed grading may adversely affect the existing or future stability of adjoining properties. The investigation shall be sufficient to outline the problems and solutions to these problems.

The soils engineer and engineering geologist shall submit written reports of their findings to the permittee and the design engineer or land surveyor. Their reports shall include but not necessarily be limited to the following minimum data based upon detailed surface and subsurface investigation:

a. The engineering geologist's report shall include a detailed geologic map showing bedrock, soil, alluvium, faults, shears, prominent joint systems, lithologic contacts, seeps or springs, soils or bedrock slumps, landslides or failures and other pertinent geologic features existing on the proposed grading site. Geologic cross-sections, prepared to reasonably depict anticipated geologic substructure, shall also be included in sufficient number and detail. The report also shall include detailed logs of all borings, test pits or other subsurface data obtained during the course of his investigation. The subsurface exploration shall extend to sufficient depth into the bedrock to expose the deepest rock affecting the proposed grading. The report shall include specific details and observations for the soils engineer's use in analysis of the stability of cut slopes in zones of shallow or perched subsurface waters that may affect slope stability.

b. The soils engineer's report shall include a map of the proposed grading site showing the locations of all subsurface exploratory test pits or borings. Detailed logs of the test pits or boring, including the approximate locations of all soil or rock samples taken for laboratory testing, shall also be included. In addition, laboratory test results, soil classification, shear strength characteristics of the soils and other pertinent soil engineering data shall be presented.

Sufficient cross-sections and cut and fill slope stability analyses shall be included to substantiate recommendations concerning the vertical height and angle of all slopes on the project.

Other aids in exploratory work may be used but subsurface exploratory work sufficient to support the findings shall be performed.

Both the engineering geologist's and soil engineer's reports shall describe the grading project as to its location, topographic relief, drainage, geologic and soils types present, the grading proposed, the effects of such grading on the site and adjoining properties, and shall contain specific conclusions concerning the feasibility and anticipated future stability of the overall project and an analysis of the property on a lot-by-lot basis. Specific recommendations for the correction of all known and/or anticipated geologic hazards on the grading project must be included.

Subject: Board Ruling--Stilt Supported Buildings Erected on Slopes Exceeding Two Horizontal to One Vertical--RR 22851

Recommendation

Approval for the Department to issue permits for stilt supported dwellings on caissons or piers where located over a fill slope exceeding two horizontal to one vertical. The Superintendent of Building shall determine that good engineering practice would permit the conditional use of such a dwelling subject to compliance with the following conditions and such other precautions found to be reasonable and necessary.

1. All footings shall be designed by a licensed engineer and extend through the fill a minimum of 3'-0" into the underlying bedrock but not less than the depth required to resist the lateral load by friction or passive resistance as determined by the foundation engineer.
2. All caissons shall be reinforced for their full length with a minimum of four No. 4 bars tied with 1/4" hoops at 12" o.c.

3. All caissons or pier footings shall be tied laterally in two directions at the ground surface with grade beams or tie beams a minimum of 12" x 12" cross-section reinforced with a minimum of four No. 4 bars tied with 1/4" hoops at 12" o.c.

4. All roof drainage is collected and conducted to the street in a non-erosive device.

5. No additional fill from the footing excavation is placed on the slope.

6. All loose brush and debris shall be removed from the site prior to starting construction.

7. The fill placed upon this property is susceptible to downhill creep which must be presumed and allowed for in the design. The designing engineer shall provide support against downhill creep which shall not be less than 1000 lbs. per linear foot acting upon each caisson or pier for the full length of its penetration through the fill. If the designing engineer or the Department finds that a greater force is probable, the design shall be modified accordingly.

The above requirements do not preclude consideration of other design methods if performed by an engineer versed in soil mechanics; and if the design is based upon exploratory evidence substantiated by engineers who are approved by the Board to make such investigations.

Exception: Where there is no fill or fill is less than 12" in depth, caissons or piers shall be designed to resist a minimum horizontal force of 1000 lbs. acting downhill on each caisson or other type of footing. Caissons or piers shall be tied together in two directions by grade beams as required in Item No. 3.

8. The site shall be planted as required by the Department to prevent surface erosion.

9. Items 1, 2, 3 and 7 listed above may be omitted if continuous footings are used throughout. Continuous footings shall be reinforced with a minimum two No. 4 bars at top and bottom of the footing.

Appendix 11-C: Excerpts of Resolution No. 5056, a Resolution of the City Council of the City of Whittier Establishing Regulations for Citizen Participation in the Federal Flood Insurance Program.

now therefore, be it resolved by the City Council of the City of Whittier:

1. That a permit shall be obtained before construction or development begins within any area of ...Mudflow Hazard...designated as Zone M on the FIRM.

2. The application for a permit shall include, but not limited by the following:

   c. A soils engineering and geology report examining data on the distribution, nature and strengths of existing soils. Conditions and recommendations for development must be certified by a registered civil engineer experienced in soils engineering....

5. The following standards shall be required for development in Mudflow Hazard Areas:

   A. Subdivision Proposals

      1. Siting, orientation and design of any improvement shall be to minimize mudflow damage.

      2. Lot designs and the location of proposed improvements shall permit accomodation of debris from mudflow without damage to improvements and with access to a street to provide for clean up and removal.

      3. An overflow route for mud and debris associated with the mudflow shall be provided in order to direct overflow away from slopes and improvements and toward safe points of discharge.

      4. Accomodation of Mudflow

         a. Design of streets shall provide for conveyance of mudflow unless other channel or debris basin is provided.

         b. If a channel is proposed as part of development its design will provide for the conveyance of the 100 year mudflow, its design will be open and it will collect and distribute flow in a manner that does not endanger properties above or below the project site.

         c. If a debris basin is proposed as part of development, its design will accommodate the 100 year mudflow plus freeboard. Access will be provided for removal of material.

Appendix 11-D: Ventura County Land Development Manual (reproduced in part).

CHAPTER 7: GRADING

7000. General. All grading for land development is subject to the Ventura County Ordinance Code (UBC Chapter 70). Although grading plans are required as part of the improvement plan package, the plan check fees, agreements, bonding, inspection and certifications are handled under the provisions of the Grading Ordinance. Appurtenances to grading (i.e., drainage devices, fences, walls, etc.) must conform to the Standard Land Development Specifications.

7107. Preliminary Grading Plan. The Developer may desire to accomplish some grading of the site prior to approval of the grading plans. In this case the grading plan may be approved, and a grading permit issued on a preliminary basis. Soils and geologic reports will be required and all other conditions of approval of a grading plan must be met. Grading plans processed in this manner must bear the following statement: CAUTION: PRELIMINARY GRADING PLAN. This plan is approved as a preliminary grading plan only. This approval does not include approval for placement of base materials, or construction of curb and gutter or any other street improvement. Grades are subject to change before approval of the road improvement plans. This note must be removed by change order at the time the road improvement plans are submitted for approval.

7108. Modification to Requirements of the Grading Ordinance. Modification of engineering requirements of the Grading Ordinance, such as steeper slopes or use of rock in shallow fills, will be made only on the basis of soils engineering reports, geological reports, etc., including recommendations for grading procedures and design criteria. Such reports must include calculations, where appropriate, allowing a quick check by County personnel. Anticipated modifications should be indicated at the tentative map stage prior to engineering design. Approval of modifications shall be obtained prior to the issuance of a grading permit for either a grading plan or a preliminary grading plan.

7109. Caution in Regard to Cut/Fill Line. Where a cut/fill line crosses a building pad, see UBC Section 29-03(e) as modified by the Ventura County Ordinance Code.

7110. Engineering Geology and Soils Engineering Reports. Engineering geology and soils engineering reports must be submitted if required by the Building Official (UBC Sections 7006(e) and (f)). Reports required by the Building Official must be submitted through the developer's engineer. Three copies of each report required plus one grading plan must be submitted to Subdivision Engineering for review. County review of such reports shall be transmitted to the Engineer as well as the Soils Engineer and Engineering Geologist, as applicable.

The following criteria are for determining whether soils and geologic reports are required:
1. A soils engineering report may be required if:
    a. The depth of cut or fill is 3 feet or greater, or
    b. The fill is to support structural footings, or
    c. An engineered cut or fill is required.

2. An engineering geology report as well as a soils engineering report may be required for projects in hillside areas and in other areas within the County wherein the County Staff Engineering Geologist believes geologic hazards may exist. A hillside area is defined as

one where any of the following conditions exist or are proposed within the project area or the area of any off-site work in connection with the proposed project:

    a. Finish cut or fill slope faces with vertical heights in excess of 10 feet.

    b. Existing slope faces steeper than 10 horizontal to 1 vertical, having a vertical height in excess of 10 feet.

7111. Employment of Engineering Professionals. The owner of land on which engineered grading is to be performed shall execute an agreement with the County to provide professional services. Such agreement shall be acknowledged by each of the professionals involved.

7112. Responsibilities of Engineering Professionals. The Engineering Professionals employed by the property owner on grading work will include the Civil Engineer, the Soils Engineer and the Engineering Geologist. The Civil Engineer's duties will include:

1. Preparation of the grading plan.
2. Design of surface drainage, irrigation and other surface features.
3. Survey and staking of the work.
4. Coordination of the other engineering professionals.
5. Provide "Rough Grading and Final Grading Certification."
6. Preparation of the "As-Built" grading plan.
7. Representing the owner for contacts by the County.
8. Certification of "As-Built" grading plan.
9. Perform such other work as is necessary to comply with the ordinance and to insure proper completion of the work in accordance with good engineering practice.

The Soils Engineer's duties will include:

1. Investigation and report on existing soil conditions.
2. Advising the Civil Engineer on soils problems affecting grading.
3. Inspection and testing of soils moved, exposed, disturbed or processed during construction. The Soils Engineer or his representative shall be on the site at all times when grading is in progress.
4. Testing completed soil masses to determine building foundation requirements.
5. Certifying that the plans and specifications are in conformance with his recommendations and to the final acceptability of the grading.
6. Design of subdrainage, erosion control, buttresses, and other soil connected features.
7. Perform such other work as is necessary to comply with the ordinance and to insure proper completion of the work in accordance with good engineering practice.

The Engineering Geologist's duties include:

1. Investigation, mapping, and report of existing geological conditions.
2. Advising The Civil Engineer and Soils Engineer on geological conditions which may affect grading.
3. Reviewing geological conditions during construction to see if modification of the grading plan is required.
4. Certifying that the plans and specifications are in conformance with his recommendations and the final grading is stable in regard to geological conditions.
5. Perform such other work as is necessary to comply with the ordinance and to insure proper completion of the work in accordance with good engineering geological practice.

As each of the engineering professionals employed in grading has a responsibility for certification of the work on completion of the project, none of the engineering professionals should be changed during the course of the project. If a change occurs, the new engineering professional must satisfy himself as to the work performed by his predecessor through certifications from his predecessor, field review, soil explorations and testing. or combinations of these or by other methods so that he will be able to certify to the entire project on completion. When changes are being made, grading will be stopped until the new professional has agreed to take responsibility for the work.

The Civil Engineer shall sign and place his registration stamp or number on the grading plan. The Soils Engineer and Engineering Geologist shall indicate, by a suitable statement, signature, registration or certification stamp of number and date on a print of the grading plan submitted to the County, that the plan incorporates all recommendations made by them.

7400. Standard Variances from the Code. Sections 7009 through 7012 of UBC allow the Building Official to approve variances from the UBC where such variance is recommended by the Soils Engineer or Engineering Geologist.

CHAPTER 8: CONSTRUCTION

8000. General. When the improvement and grading plans have been signed and the permits issued by the County Surveyor, the County responsibility for control of the land development is transferred from Subdivision Engineering to Construction Inspection. A construction engineer and an inspector will be assigned by the County to watch the construction to insure that the grading and the construction of road improvements meet the minimum requirements of County ordinances and standards. This assignment in no way relieves the developer from the responsibility for inspection and supervision of construction, or of any responsibility for meeting the requirements of the plans, permits, Grading Ordinances, and the Standard Land Development Specifications or for assuming construction in accordance with recommendations of the Soils Engineers and Engineering Geologist.

8300. Grading Inspection. Inspection of grading is accomplished under the Grading Ordinance. It is emphasized that the Grading Ordinance is directed particularly to grading of private property, and that the responsibilities of the Developer, Developer's Engineer, Developer's Soils Engineer. and Developer's Engineering Geologist are assigned under the Grading Ordinance. Omissions from the plans of any work required by the Grading Ordinance will not excuse the developer from any responsibility for compliance.

8006. Grading Reports. The Building Official requires that the compaction test data, including results, location and elevation, be available for inspection on the site at all times during business hours: or, reports are to be mailed daily to the Building Official's designated representative. The method of reporting shall be determined at the preconstruction conference at the option of the Soils Engineer.

The Building Official requires sufficient inspection by the Engineering Geologist to assure that all geologic conditions have been adequately considered. Where geologic conditions warrant, the Building Official may require interim geologic reports. These reports may be required to include, but need not be limited to reporting, inspection of cut slopes, canyons during clearing operations for ground water and earth material conditions, benches prior to placement of fill, and possible spring locations.

8309. As-Built Grading Plans. Upon completion of the grading work, the Civil Engineer shall prepare an "As-Built" grading plan. The Soils Engineer and the Engineering Geologist shall indicate by a suitable statement, signature, and date on a print of the "As-Built" grading plan that it agrees with the results of the work for which they were responsible as determined by field inspection. The Civil Engineer shall indicate on the reproducible copy of the "As-Built" grading plan that he has received from the Soils Engineer and the Engineering Geologist and has submitted to the County the signed prints of the grading plans prepared by them. The Civil Engineer shall also sign the reproducible "As-Built" grading plan, certifying that it is correct.

GRADING CONTRACTOR CERTIFICATION

Job Address or

Tract No. ------------------------ Locality ----------------------

Owner --------------------------- Permit No. --------------------

I certify that the grading was done in accordance with the plans and specifications, the grading ordinance, and the recommendations of the Civil Engineer, Soils Engineer and Engineering Geologist. It is understood that this certification includes only those aspects of the work that can be determined by me, as a competent grading contractor, without special equipment or professional skills.

Grading Contractor -------------------------------------

License No. ---

Instructions: The owner shall sign if the grading was not done by a licensed grading contractor.

Appendix 11-E: Excerpt from the Uniform Building Code.

Paragraph 7009. CUTS

(a) **General.** Unless otherwise recommended in the approved soils engineering and/or engineering gwology report, cuts shall conform to the provisions of this section.

(b) **Slope.** The slope of cut surfaces shall be no steeper than is safe for the intended use. Cut slopes shall be no steeper than two horizontal to one vertical.

(c) **Drainage and Terracing.** Drainage and terracing shall be provided as required by Paragraph 7012.

Paragraph 7010. FILLS

(a) **General.** Unless otherwise recommended in the approved soils engineering report, fills shall conform to the provisions of this section. In the absence of an approved soils engineering report, these provisions may be waived for minor fills not intended to support structures.

(b) **Fill Location.** Fill slopes shall not be constructed on natural slopes steeper than two to one.

(c) **Preparation of Ground.** The ground surface shall be prepared to receive fill by removing vegetation, noncomplying fill, topsoil, and other unsuitable materials, scarifying to provide a bond with the new fill, and, where slopes are steeper than five to one and the height is greater than five feet, by benching into sound bedrock or other competent material as determined by the soils engineer. The bench under the toe of a fill on a slope steeper than five to one shall be at least 10-feet wide. The area beyond the toe of the fill shall be sloped for sheet overflow, or a paved drain shall be provided. Where fill is to be placed over a cut, the bench under the toe of fill shall be at least 10-feet wide, but the cut must be made before placing fill and approved by the soils engineer and engineering geologist as a suitable foundation for fill. Unsuitable soil is soil which, in the opinion of the building official or the civil engineer or the soils engineer or the geologist, is not competent to support other soil or fill, to support structures, or to satisfactorily perform the other functions for which the soil is intended.

(d). **Fill Material.** Detrimental amounts of organic material shall not be permitted in fills. Except as permitted by the building official, no rock or similar irreducible material with a maximum dimension greater than 12 inches shall be buried or placed in fills.

> *EXCEPTION: The building official may permit placement of larger rock when the soils engineer properly devises a method of placemnt, continuously inspects its placemnt, and approves the fill stability. The following conditions also apply:*

A. Prior to issuance of the grading permit, potential rock disposal areas shall be delineated on the grading plan.

B. Rock sizes greater than 12 inches in maximum dimensions shall be 10 feet or more below grade, measured vertically.

C. Rocks shall be placed so as to assure filling of all voids with fines.

(e) **Compaction.** All fills shall be compacted to a minimum of 90 percent of maximum density, as determined by UBC Standard No 70-1. Field density shall be determined in accordance with UBS Standard No. 70-2 or equivalent, as approved by the building official.

(f) **Slope.** The slope of fill surfaces shall be no steeper than is safe for the intended use. Fill slopes shall be no steeper than two horizontal to one vertical.

(g) **Drainage and Terracing.** Drainage and terracing shall be provided and the area above fill slopes and the surfaces of terraces shall be graded and paved as required by Paragraph 7012.

Paragraph 7011. SETBACKS

(a) **General.** The setbacks and other restrictions specified by this section are minimum and may be increased by the building official or by the recommendation of a civil engineer, soils engineer, or engineering geologist, if necessary for safety and stability or to prevent damage of adjacent properties from deposition or erosion or to provide access for slope maintenance and drainage. Retaining walls may be used to reduce the required setbacks when approved by the building official.

(b) **Setbacks from Property Lines.** The tops of cuts and toes of fill slopes shall be set back from the outer boundaries of the permit area, including slope-right areas and easements.

(c) **Design Standards for Setbacks.** Setbacks between graded slopes (cut or fill) and structures shall be provided.

Paragraph 7012 DRAINAGE AND TERRACING.

(a) **General.** Unless otherwise indicated on the approved grading plan, drainage facilities and terracing shall conform to the provision of this section.

(b) **Terrace.** Terraces at least six feet in width shall be established at not more than 30-foot vertical intervals on all cut or fill slopes to control surface drainage and debris, except that where only one terrace is required, it shall be at mid-height. For cut or fill slopes greater than 60 feet and up to 120 feet in vertical height, one terrace at approximately mid-height shall be 12 feet in width. Terrace widths and spacing for cut and fill slopes greater than 120 feet in height shall be designed by the civil engineer and approved by the building official. Suitable access shall be provided to permit proper cleaning and maintenance.

Swales or ditches on terraces shall have a minimum gradient of five percent and must be paved with reinforced concrete not less than three inches in thickness or an approved equal paving. They shall have a minimum depth at the deepest point of one foot and a minimum paved width of five feet. A single run of swale or ditch shall not collect runoff from a tributary area exceeding 13,500 square feet (projected) without discharging into a down drain.

(c) **Subsurface Drainage.** Cut and fill slopes shall be provided with subsurface drainage as necessary for stability.

(d) **Disposal.** All drainage facilities shall be designed to carry waters to the nearest practicable drainage way approved by the building official and/or other appropriate jurisdiction as a safe place to deposit such waters. Erosion of ground in the area of discharge shall be prevented by installation of nonerosive down drains or other devices.

Building pads shall have a drainage gradient of two percent toward approved drainage facilities, unless waived by the building official.

EXCEPTION: The gradient from the building pad may be one percent if all of the following conditions exist throughout the permit area:

A. No proposed fills are greater than 10 feet in maximum depth.
B. No proposed finish cut or fill slope faces have a vertical height in excess of 10 feet.
C. No existing slope faces which have a slope face steeper than 10 horizontally to one vertically have a vertical height in excess of 10 feet.

(e) **Interceptor Drains.** Paved interceptor drains shall be installed along the top of all cut slopes where the tributary drainage area above slopes towards the cut and has a drainage path greater than 40 feet measured horizontally. Interceptor drains shall be paved with a minimum of three inches of concrete or gunite and reinforced. They shall have a minimum depth of twelve inches and a minimum paved width of 30 inches measured horizontally across the drain. The slope of drain shall be approved by the building official.

Paragraph 7013. EROSION CONTROL

(a) **Slopes.** The faces of cut and fill slopes shall be prepared and maintained to control against erosion. This control may consist of effective planting. The protection for the slopes shall be installed as soom as practicable and prior to calling for final approval. Where cut slopes are not subject to erosion due to the erosion-resistant character of the materials, such protection may be omitted.

(b) **Other Devices.** Where necessary, check dams, cribbing, riprap, or other devices or methods shall be employed to control erosion and provide safety.

Appendix 11-F: What the Buyer, Builder, or Homeowner Should Look For. Excerpt from a report on landsliding for Allegheny County, PA, Briggs *et al.* 1975..

The buyer, builder, or homeowner must always bear in mind that areas susceptible to landslides commonly are larger than most indiviual properties. Thus, it pays to look not only at the property in question but also at adjacent areas, particularly those upslope and downslope. If the property slopes more steeply than about 15 percent (15 feet of drop or rise vertically in 100 feet of horizontal distance), or if adjacent uphill or downhill slopes (or both) are significantly steeper than the slope of the property, site examination should be made. In addition, if the property is on relatively flat ground on a ridge top or in a valley, but close to a fairly steep slope, an examination of the slope is recommended.

(1) *Cracks in buildings.* Most older buildings have minor cracks, but these probably result largely from normal settlement. In general, the fact that a building is old and shows no significant damage is an indication that the building probably will remain undamaged by landsliding. Many or large cracks in newer structures are reasons for concern, although the cause of cracking may well be something other than landsliding. Major cracks commonly are repaired by owners, but evidence of repair usually is visible on close examination. Wet basements may be evidence of cracks in the foundation.

(2) *Cracks in brick walls around yards and other outside brick and concrete features.* Unlike buildings, which generally are set in bedrock, most yard walls and other ancillary features rest on soil. They thus are sensitive to creep which can cause cracking or can pull such features away from structures.

(3) *Doors and windows that jam.* A door that sticks or otherwise does not seem to fit well or a sash window that jams may be evidence that the frame of a house has been warped.

(4) *Retaining walls, fences, curbs, gas meters, posts supporting parches, and other features out of plumb or not aligned in a normal way.*

(7) *Tilted trees, grapevines, reeds.* Trees are probably somewhat less reliable indicators of slope movement than are manmade objects, for trees on slopes tend to bend outward somewhat as they seek sunlight. However, trees leaning at appreciable angles or numbers of trees leaning in different directions strongly suggest areas of landsliding or strong creep. Many grapevines and reeds have been observed on many prehistoric landslide deposits, perhaps as a result of water conditions within the deposits. They thus are general indicators of possbile instability.

(8) *Tilted utility poles and taut or sagging wires.* Most utility poles are more or less vertical and aligned when new, and wires between poles usually sag uniformly, so appreciable tilting of poles and variations in amount of sag of wires between adjacent poles are abnormal and noteworthy.

(9) *Cracks in the ground.* Cracks more or less parallel to a slope usually are indications that the slope is moving.

(10) *Steplike ground features.* Slumping of ground usually results in steplike scarps that may range from very low to many feet high. When relatively new, the "risers" of the scarps usually expose fresh earth. Older scarps may have subdued angles because of ero-

sion and may be vegetated, making them more difficult to identify. Whether old or new, these features are evidence of unstable conditions.

(11) *Hummocky ground.* Hummocks, low mounds, are common irregularly spaced features of the toes and lower ground surfaces of both prehistoric and recent landslides. They do not occur naturally on any other surfaces in Allegheny County.

(12) Water seeps. Seeps and springs are very common at the toes of landslide deposits. Water from seeps on upper slopes may saturate the ground and so contribute to the mobility of downslope materials.

SELECTED REFERENCES ON FLOODING DUE TO MUDSLIDES

California Geology Staff, 1979, *Slope Instability and Debris Flows*. Prepared from studies conducted by F.H. Weber, Jr. and J. A. Treiman. California Geology 32.

Campbell, R.H., 1975, *Soil Slips, Debris Flows, and Rainstorms in the Santa Monica Mountains and Vicinity, Southern California*, U.S. Geological Survey Miscellaneous Field Studies Map MF-1406, Scale 1:62,500.

Cleveland, G.B., 1973, *Fire + Rain = Mudflow: Big Sur 1972*. California Geology 26: 127-135.

County of San Diego, 1977, *Storm Report: Tropical Storm Doreen*. Augusts 15-17, 1977. San Diego, California: County Dept. of Sanitation and Flood Control.

Cummins, J., 1981, *Mudflows Resulting from the May 18, 1980, Eruption of Mount St. Helens*. USGS Circular #850-B. Washington, D.C.: U.S. Dept. of Interior.

Davis, J.D., 1979, *Engineering Methodology for Mudflow Analysis*. Preliminary Report. Los Angeles, California: Los Angeles Flood Control District.

Douglas, J.S., D.T. Larson, D.H. Hoggan and T.L. Glover, 1980, *Flood Damage Mitigation in Utah*. Water Resources Planning Series UWFL/P-80-01. Logan, Utah: Utah Water Researach Laboratory, Utah State University.

Early, D. and W.J. Kockelman, no date, *Reducing Landslide Hazards: A Guide for Planners*. American Planning Advisory Service Report Nol 359. Chicago, Illinois: APA.

Ellen, S., D.M. Peterson and G.O. Reed, 1982, *Map Showing Areas Susceptible to Different Hazards from Shallow Landsliding in Marin County, California*. USGS Miscellaneous Field Studies Map MP-1406, Scale 1:62,500.

Evans, J.R. and C.H. Gray, Jr. (editors), 1971, *Analysis of Mudslide Risk in Southern Ventura County, California*. CDMG Release 72-73. Sacramento, California: Division of Mines and Geology.

Fleming, R.W. and F.A. Taylor, 1980, *Estimating the Costs of Landslide Damage in the United States*. USGS Circular 832. Washington, D.C.: U.S. Government Printing Office.

Glancey, P.A., 1969, *A Mudflow in the Second Creek Drainage, Lake tAHOE Basin, Nevada and its Relation to Sedimentation and Urbanization*. USGS Professional Paper No. 650-C. Washington, D.C.: U.S. Government Printing Office.

Kaliser, B.N., 1983, *The Davis County Experience*. Survey Notes 17:10-11. Salt Lake City, Utah: Utah Geological and Mineral Survey.

Krohn, J.P. and J.E. Slosson, 1976, *Landslide Potential in the United States.* California Geology, 29(10): 224-231.

Lombard, R.E., 1981, *Channel Conditions in the Lower Toutle and Cowlitz Rivers Resulting from the Mudflows of May 18, 1980.* USGS Circular #850-C. Washington, D.C.: U.S. Department of the Interior.

Los Angeles County Flood Control District, 1979, *Mudflow Methodology. Los Angeles, California*: Los Angeles County Flood Control District.

Mears, A.I., 1977, *Debris-flow Hazard Analysis and Mitigation: An Example from Glenwood Springs, Colorado.* Information Series No. 8. Denver, Colorado: Colorado Geological Survey.

Morton, D.M. and R.H. Campbell, 1978, *Cyclic Landsliding at Wrightwood. Southern California - A Preliminary Report.* USGS Open File Report 78-1079. Washington, D.C.: U.S. Department of Interior.

National Oceanic and Atmospheric Administration, 1981, *The Disastrous Southern California and Central Arizona Floods, Flash Floods and Mudslides of February 1980*: A Report to the Administrator. Natural Disastger Survey Report NWS-81-1. Silver Spring, Maryland: National Weather Service.

National Research Council, 1974, Panel on Methodology for Delineating Mudslide Hazard Areas. *Methodology for Delineating Mudslide Hazard Areas.* Washington, D.C.: National Academy of Sciences.

------, 1982, Committee on Methodologies for Predicting Mudflow Areas. *Selecting a Methodology for Delineating Mudslide Hazard Areas for the National Flood Insurance Program.* Washington, D.C.: National Academy Press.

Schuster, R.L.,, 1978, Introduction. In: R.L. Schuster and R.J. Krizek, (editors) *Landslides, Analysis and Control.* Special Report 176. Washington, D.C.: National Research Council, Transportation Research Board.

Slosson, J.E. and J.P. Krohn, 1979, *AEG Building Code Review - Mudflow/Debris Flow Damage, February 1978 Storm - Los Angeles Area.* California Geology 32:8-11.

Task Group on Landslides and Other Ground Failures, 1981, *Report to the Commission on Sociotechnical Systems*, National Research Council. Washington, D.C.: National Research Council.

U. S. Geological Survey, 1982, *Goals and Tasks of the Landslide Part of a Ground-Failure Hazards Reduction Program*, Circular 880. Alexandria, Virginia: U. S. Geological Survey.

------, 1983, *Potential for Debris Flow and Debris Flood Along the Wasatch Front*, Open File
    Report 83-635.

☆ U.S. GOVERNMENT PRINTING OFFICE: 1993 — 7 2 3- 3 5 2/ 8 0 4 5 9